Inspired and Edited by

Philip McMillan Browse

Heligan's First Horticultural Director

with a Foreword by

John Willis

descendant of the Tremaynes
who created the Gardens

and Contributions by **Heligan Staff**
who now look after them

Contents

Foreword
by John Willis

Rhododendron falconeri – *a Fitch lithograph copied from* The Rhododendrons of Sikkim-Himalaya 1849–51 *by J.D. Hooker, once in the Library of Heligan House (left), and a Heligan Survivor, grown from seed collected and sent back from Sikkim by Hooker*

Heligan Survivors is a book whose idea encapsulates for me everything that makes Heligan such a special place – that is, its individuality and character, which were shaped over the generations and which still exude their vital force today.

Academics may theorise about the development of the English landscape, but what this beautiful book shows is how it takes the vision and energy of individuals – their personal passions and ideals – to create a truly enduring legacy. To explore this through the individual stories of some of the plant 'survivors' – specimens, indeed, that would have been recognised as old friends when they were old by the pioneering plantsmen who first raised them – is an inspiring idea, as it explores the very root of Heligan. The fact that their stories are told by so many individual members of staff at Heligan is testament to the continuing passion of individual commitment which proves – if proof were needed – that the Gardens are indeed in good hands.

When I first came to know Heligan – in the days when the gardens were literally lost and forgotten by all but a tiny few – its future seemed bleak and the plant survivors a small and beleaguered band struggling valiantly against overwhelming odds.

But now the odds are different. After 15 years of dedication, care and sheer hard work, the Heligan Survivors have gained a new lease of life, and they and their progeny have set the seed for generations to come.

I, for one, am deeply grateful.

Spring 2007

The Tremaynes and the Gardens at Heligan

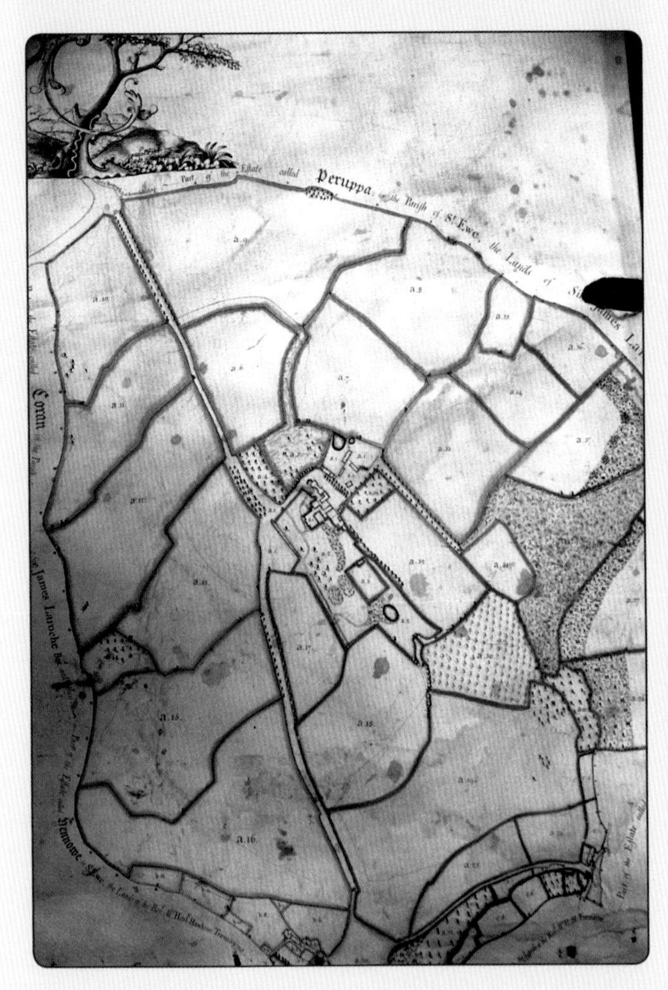

Clockwise from left: A plan of Heligan by William Hole, 1777; Heligan House, 1844; the Jungle, early twentieth century

The horticultural triumph that was to become the Lost Gardens of Heligan was developed over 150 years by four generations of the Tremayne family. Henry Hawkins Tremayne (born 1741) became Squire in 1766, and the initial success was the result of his endeavours over 63 years.

Henry Hawkins married a local heiress, Harriet Hearle, which brought him a third interest in the extensive Hearle estates and mining businesses. With the subsequent deaths of distant relatives he came into estates at Croan and at Sydenham in Devon, and when he died was significantly wealthy. Henry became important and influential in the political and commercial circles in Cornwall, and aspired to create a great garden to enhance his home and reputation.

He planted extensive tree shelterbelts on the East and West, and in 1785 toured gardens in the South of the Country to further his appreciation. He visited Prior Park, Blenheim, Painshill, Stowe, Warwick Castle, the Leasowes, and Hestercombe – where Bampfylde and his garden greatly impressed him. On his return he set about getting rid of the previously fashionable, formal parterre gardens to the South of the House, and began merging the garden with the landscape in the *ferme ornée* tradition. He planted further extensive woodland and laid out miles of rides to allow his family and visitors to enjoy the countryside and local scenery. By the 1820s Henry had developed a rapidly maturing garden, and Heligan was acknowledged as an impressive example of contemporary landscape taste.

Henry died in 1829, having established the structural framework of the Gardens we know today. He was succeeded by his son, John Hearle Tremayne, who for 40 years was a local MP. But he still had much time for Heligan. His primary interests were the woodlands and farm, but he also had a significant interest in the Gardens and, dwelling for much of his time in London, was almost certainly a member of the Horticultural Society and a frequenter of their

Gardens at Chiswick. He added plants to the Garden – most notably *Cornus capitata*. This plant was first cultivated in England at Heligan. Sir Anthony Buller, MP for Liskeard, had been on an expedition to Nepal and collected seed (presumably from the lower slopes of the Himalaya), which he gave to John Hearle Tremayne in 1825. It proved a prolific, decorative and successful plant, and by 1832 four hundred plants lined the new Long Drive.

John Hearle Tremayne had married Caroline, sister of Sir Charles Lemon of Carclew, and through this connection the Hooker Rhododendrons came to Heligan – whether before or after his death is not known. Sir Charles was also a local MP and a familiar of J.D. Hooker. This was a period of consolidation for the Estate.

John Hearle was succeeded by his son, John Tremayne, in 1851, and lived at Heligan for 50 years until his death in 1901, making a dramatic contribution to the Heligan we know today. Much of the ornamental planting of trees and shrubs (including the Hooker Rhododendrons and the Camellia collection), which still survives, dates from this time – the great Victorian Imperial period of plant exploration and introduction. Cornwall's climate is particularly benign, and suits many of the less-hardy introductions. Other dominant plants in the gardens at Heligan, dating from the later part of his tenure, include the Tree Ferns, distributed by Treseders in the late 1890s, and the Trachycarpus palms, whose planting must reasonably date from after the Great Freeze of April 1891.

At an early age John had contracted a severe bone disease, and spent the rest of his life on crutches or in a wheelchair. He had the time and the inclination to pursue his interests in the Estate and, in particular, in Horticulture. He was proud of his collection of tree rhododendrons, and in later life was interested in their hybridisation. During his tenure Mrs Tremayne's Flower Garden (the Sundial Garden) was laid out – the current design favours the likely planting *c.*1880. He also became interested in orchids, and the collapsing, 'stand alone' greenhouse, still extant just inside the north door of the Walled Flower Garden in 1990, was their home.

In 1891 John's son, John Claude (Jack) Tremayne, returned from living in Italy to join his father at Heligan. He was of an artistic bent, and a talented plantsman, and was the architect of what we call the Jungle. He was also responsible for the construction of the Ravine: in those days a 'rockery' was to show off the rocks – plants were incidental. John Claude succeeded as Squire on his father's death in 1901, and prior to 1906/7 created the Italian Garden (the Suntrap Garden), with many new exotics. Most notable of these today is the Chinese Gooseberry (*Actinidia chinensis*), or Kiwi Fruit – an E.H. Wilson introduction obtained from Veitch. He also planted (*inter alia*) the *Davidia involucrata* and the *Magnolia delavayi*.

Left to right: Henry Hawkins Tremayne and John Hearle Tremayne (top); John Tremayne and John Claude (Jack) Tremayne (above)

Jack Tremayne moved out of Heligan during the Great War, when it was used as a military convalescent hospital. He returned in 1919, but soon went back to his wartime base at Croan (so many gardeners and estate staff had been killed, and he 'couldn't live with the ghosts'), and thence to Italy again. Heligan House was rented. The era of unlimited labour and wealth was gone, and the tenants' best efforts could not reverse the slow decline. The Second World War also saw the House vacated and again, after the war, it was rented. The decline continued, and by the mid-1960s the House and Garden were in poor condition. In 1970 the House was sold and turned into flats. Most of the supporting buildings were sold and converted for residential use; the Garden was abandoned. Jack had died in 1949, after which the contents of Heligan House were auctioned off.

In 1990 the Gardens were seen by Tim Smit ... and the rest, as they say, 'is History'.

The Nurserymen and the Plant Collectors

In 1768 John Veitch came from Scotland to be Head Gardener to Sir Thomas Acland at Killerton House. Seeing the rise of landscape 'improvement' and the mania for new plants, he opened a nursery at nearby Budlake in 1778. This move established a dynasty that dominated nursery production in the second half of the nineteenth century, and which was also ended by the Great War.

As Exeter expanded, so did the business. John's son, James, moved to Mount Radford in 1832, and then to London, purchasing a nursery in Chelsea in 1853, which his son, James junior, opened as the Royal Exotic Nursery. However, the Veitchs' importance lies mainly in their entrepreneurial involvement and foresight in employing exclusive plant collectors. Their canny investment in 22 collectors, including the Cornish Lobb brothers, Richard Pearce and E.H. Wilson, paid huge dividends for them and for Horticulture in general.

The Tremaynes of Heligan patronised the Veitchs. Jack Tremayne purchased the latest novelties from the Royal Exotic Nursery in the Edwardian period, and particular plants in the Gardens suggest regular purchases of Veitch plants over the previous 50 years.

The first Veitch collector was William Lobb. In the 1840s he travelled extensively in South and Central America, sending back commercial quantities of the seed of the Monkey Puzzle (*Araucaria araucana*). Then he went to the West Coast of the USA, from where he brought back seeds of the Wellingtonia (*Sequoiadendron giganteum*). His brother Thomas was a hugely influential collector in the tropics and sub-tropics of South East Asia, with orchids a speciality. At the turn of the century, Veitch was the first to employ Ernest Henry 'Chinese' Wilson, who became perhaps the most successful plant collector ever.

There was a similar rise in fortune for the nurseries of the Treseder family. James Treseder, a market gardener and seedsman, established himself at

The rise of Horticulture as an embellishment to a gentleman's property developed in the first half of the eighteenth century, with the evolution of a positive approach to landscape management and enhancement, fuelled by the exotic plants sent back by the burgeoning business of plant collecting. At first plants arrived chiefly for use in the temperate landscape, particularly from North America and the Orient. In the nineteenth century, as transport became more sophisticated, and the world more accessible, destinations included Australasia, the Cape and South America.

Technological evolution encouraged the continuing refinement of greenhouse construction and heating systems. Coupled with an increased understanding of cultivation, this permitted the management of plants from more benign climates. And the advancement of Science brought an understanding of hybridisation, leading to even more splendid plants.

At Heligan the development of the Grounds mirrored this state, as four generations of the Tremayne family embellished their surroundings, each improving on the efforts of their predecessors. This was made possible by the parallel commercial production of the new plants to satisfy an ever-increasing demand. The rise and fall (which came with the end of the Great War) of the Gentleman's Garden was reflected in the Nursery Industry, where family businesses followed in tandem. None reflects this more than the House of Veitch.

Left to right: John, James and James Veitch (junior), E.H. Wilson (top); James Treseder, David Douglas (middle); Archibald Menzies, Robert Fortune (bottom)

Moresk, Truro in 1839. Apart from a period (1881–95) in Australia, the family were nurserymen until 1979. Like the Veitchs, they first produced native trees and shrubs for landscaping. As fashions changed, his son John used the climatic advantage of the far South West to create a commercial palette of exotic plants.

The Nursery's main claim to fame, in terms of the introduction of exotica, and in relation to Heligan, was the large-scale importation of Tree Ferns and other Australasian plants from the late 1890s until the Great War. They also provided the material for extensive plantings of the palm *Trachycarpus fortunei*, and the New Zealand Cabbage Tree, *Cordyline australis*.

Plant hunting was not the sole prerogative of nurserymen. Interested 'natural philosophers' had been collecting since the late eighteenth century. One of the earliest and most significant was the Scot, Archibald Menzies, a Royal Naval surgeon-cum-naturalist, who accompanied Captain George Vancouver on HMS *Discovery* on his circumnavigation. Setting out in 1790, they followed Cook's route via the Cape and Australia, to map the North West Coast of the Americas, and to fill in blanks left by Cook. It was Menzies who first collected the Monkey Puzzle (*Araucaria araucana*) in Chile and who first described the Douglas Fir, which, although introduced later by David Douglas, perpetuates his memory in its Latin name *Pseudotsuga menziesii*.

The continuing expansion of interests of the recently formed London Horticultural Society (which was founded in 1804) included the commissioning of collectors for the benefit of the Society and its members. One of the most successful was David Douglas, another Scot and a protégé of William Hooker. He travelled in the virtually unknown and uncharted territory of the West Coast of North America and its hinterland – from British Columbia to California – in the late 1820s and early 1830s. Apart from the important introduction of seed of the Douglas Fir, he collected seeds of many pines and a wide variety of plants now commonplace – over 240 species in all.

In 1841 another Scot, Robert Fortune, became Superintendent of the Horticultural Society's Hothouse Department in the Gardens at Chiswick. He was then appointed their Collector in China. Arriving in 1843 he spent three years travelling extensively, collecting a host of interesting and beautiful plants. He succeeded largely because he took the trouble to learn Mandarin, disguising himself by shaving his head and adopting local dress. He made a second trip to China in 1848, this time on behalf of the Honourable East India Company (HEIC), to obtain tea plants and seeds in order to allow the establishment of tea production in British India. He was so successful that he was able to send back some 20,000 tea plants, all growing in Wardian cases, which were established at Darjeeling – the foundation of the Indian tea industry. It was during this trip, on passage through the Chusan Islands *en route* into the Yangtze, that he first saw and collected the hardy palm *Trachycarpus fortunei* – now a regular landscape feature in the milder niches of cold temperate climates.

Sir Joseph Dalton Hooker OM, FRS

Rhododendron valley in Sikkim

Confinement hut beneath the Rajah's residence

The evolution of the Gardens at Heligan has been largely a function of the endeavours of a resident horticultural dynasty – the Tremayne family – over some 150 years. However, since the second half of the nineteenth century, it has also been inextricably connected with a certain Joseph Dalton Hooker, who introduced to cultivation the majority of the 'tree rhododendrons' that dominate the garden landscape of Heligan and constitute one of the most impressive collections of these plants still existing. These large, tree-like shrubs have become a signature plant in the Gardens, and have survived largely because of the increasing neglect they experienced in the second half of the twentieth century – the surrounding over- and undergrowth protecting them from the vagaries and extremes of the climate. This allowed them to reach an unprecedented maturity and size for plants grown in (albeit unmanaged) cultivation. However, the original plants are now 150 years old, and are inevitably reaching the end of their life.

Joseph Dalton Hooker was the son of William Hooker, who was to become the first Director of Kew and (eventually) Sir William. From an early age he was bent on travelling the world and exploring for plants. But because of his lack of personal wealth (unlike Banks and Darwin), he had to take those opportunities that presented themselves. He studied at the University of Glasgow (where his father was Professor of Botany), and at the age of 22 graduated in medicine, which would allow him to obtain a post as an Assistant Surgeon on Royal Navy ships mounting expeditions of exploration – a not unusual career move for an aspiring scientist without personal income at that time. His first opportunity came as he completed his studies.

Through the good offices of his father and grandfather he was able to canvass for, and obtain, the appointment as the Assistant Surgeon and Botanist on the *Erebus*, as part of the ship's company of Captain (later Sir) James Clark Ross. This epic and hugely successful four-year expedition was mounted to explore in and around Antarctica – principally to map the precise position of the southern Magnetic Pole. This provided Joseph with unrivalled opportunities to observe a wide range of plants, as the expedition visited Kerguelen Island, Australasia, Cape Horn and the Falkland Islands in the periods between the major sorties inside the Antarctic Circle. He was particularly interested in mosses, liverworts and lichens, but his devotion to Science included collecting and observing higher plants and seaweeds, as well as trawling for, and describing, many sea creatures. He was very able at pencil drawing, and much of his work is greatly enhanced by this talent. This expedition also confirmed his previously held interest in the distribution of plant species.

On his return in 1843 he began working on the writing up and publication of various aspects of his work. During this time he became an intimate of Charles Darwin, providing him with much information on plants and their importance and relationships. With Thomas Henry Huxley, he was eventually to be one of Evolution's champions. These friendships, with both men, were to last for all their lifetimes.

Despite these extensive travels, however, he was still consumed with the desire to explore for plants. In 1847 an opportunity arose to make a trip to India, and Joseph was granted a small government stipend to facilitate this. He sailed on the ship which was taking Lord Dalhousie (the new Governor-General) to India. Evidently he was pleasant and sociable, for Lord Dalhousie added him to his personal entourage from Alexandria – so reducing diplomatic difficulties and making the passage easier and more tolerable. The same good fortune was also to his advantage in India itself. His particular remit was to explore in the Himalaya, and late in 1848 he sought the permissions necessary to make an expedition into the otherwise closed country of Sikkim. He prepared for this by spending valuable time observing the local plants, and learning from the celebrated scholar and naturalist Brian Hodgson, at his residence in the hills near Darjeeling. The pair became close friends, but Hodgson's health deteriorated and he was unable to take part in the expedition. Joseph was instead accompanied by the local Government agent, Archibald Campbell.

Joseph was away from England for four years, and travelled through much of India, observing, collecting and cataloguing the plants, observing the culture and describing the Country.

The lasting memorial of this trip is the great variety of tree rhododendrons that he discovered and collected during this relatively short, but interesting, hazardous and extraordinarily eventful expedition into Sikkim. The fruits of his efforts – the rhododendron seeds which he had collected – arrived safely at Kew in 1849.

Sir Charles Lemon was a familiar of Hooker, and contributed towards the expenses of his expedition. Thus, in 1851, seed and seedlings found their way to Carclew, and from there a share was sent to Heligan. They were eventually planted out around the House, down the Rides and on Flora's Green in the Northern Gardens, and in what was to develop as the Jungle, South of the House. John Tremayne was a keen farmer and horticulturist, and indulged in hybridisation of his rhododendrons. By the turn of the century he had produced many fine seedlings which were also planted out all over the Gardens. Today they present a nightmare in trying to determine which is what, as no planting plans (if ever there were any) survive.

J.D. Hooker

Hooker was back in England in 1851, and although he had already achieved considerable celebrity, he was to achieve far greater fame both as a botanist and for eventually succeeding his father as Director of Kew. He died in 1911, at the age of 94.

Rhododendron Names

As a young man in India with little money, Hooker was unable to provide presents for his benefactors. So he arranged for as many of them as possible to be remembered, by naming newly discovered species of plants after them or their wives. Unfortunately, not all of these names are now extant, as the arcane machinations of the plant taxonomist find prior names, or the concept of a particular species is altered.

- *aucklandii* – for Lord Auckland, First Lord of the Admiralty, facilitator of his trip and the stipend
- *campbelliae* – for Mrs Archibald Campbell, wife of the Governor-General's Agent and Superintendent of Darjeeling; also Hooker's companion in Sikkim
- *dalhousiae* – for Lady Dalhousie, wife of the Governor-General of India
- *falconeri* – for Dr Hugh Falconer, Superintendent of the Botanic Garden at Calcutta, expatriate Scotsman, who acted as agent for Hooker in forwarding plant material to England and sending on to him books, materials, etc.
- *hodgsonii* – for Brian Hodgson, Sanskrit and Buddhist scholar, naturalist and friend
- *thomsonii* – for Dr Thomas Thomson, Hooker's companion for the last two years of his trip, who accompanied him back to England and collaborated on the subsequent work.

The Sikkim Rhododendrons

arboreum, *barbatum*, *campylocarpum*, *falconeri*, *grande*, *griffithianum*, *hodgsonii*, *niveum*, *thomsonii*, etc.

Actinidia chinensis

Actinidia chinensis
in the Italian Garden today

The Italian Garden
c.1910

One of the earliest defining moments in the successful resurrection of 'The Lost Gardens of Heligan' was the visit of the team from BBC TV's *Gardeners' World* in Autumn 1991. Their principal interest was to view the state of wilderness and demonstrate, for viewers, the challenge – but they also hoped to show something of our efforts at the beginnings of restoration. Thus, in order to satisfy their needs, it was decided to present a small cameo and recover the Italian Garden. This process uncovered two individuals of an uncommon climbing plant, *Actinidia chinensis* (nowadays *A. deliciosa*), growing closely together on the wall by the corner of the Summerhouse.

These had been unrestrained for so long and free of any controlling management that they had entrenched and taken off. They had virtually demolished the Summerhouse by their weight and the sinuous exploration of their branches through the tiles. Then, having burst free, they had taken off to the top of an adjacent tree, to a height of more than 40ft.

As part of the recovery programme during that Autumn, they were cut right back to below the top of the wall – at a height of about 7ft – so that the weight of material could be more readily cleared. As soon as this had been accomplished they began to bleed, and in such copious quantities that an allusion to 'stuck pigs' came to mind! This bleeding went on and on and on – for days and days and then, when it eventually ceased, red pustules erupted all over the stems. By this stage there was great consternation that death was imminent; but come the Spring, the buds burst as normal and vigorous replacement growth proceeded as though nothing had happened!

The Italian (or Suntrap) Garden had been designed by Squire Jack Tremayne and, from available contemporary photographs, it seems was finished, and in use, by 1906/7. This helps to date the arrival of the Actinidia at Heligan, and it is reasonable to assume that both were part of the original plantings. It was a new introduction at that time, and plants were being offered for sale by Messrs James Veitch & Sons. These plants had been raised from seed collected by E.H. Wilson, during his trip (1899–1901) to China to collect seeds of *Davidia involucrata*. It was first offered for sale in the Veitch catalogue of 1904, as the 'Chinese Gooseberry'. The sobriquet 'Kiwi Fruit' has only become attached to it in recent years, as a result of the commercial exploitation of the crop in New Zealand.

In China it is a fairly common native plant, chiefly on the fringes of woodlands, and with a fairly wide distribution through the more northern parts of the country to Amurland. It was very abundant in the valley of the Yangtze, and it was here that Wilson would have seen it around his houseboat-base at Ichang. The fruits were sold on the markets in China, and were apparently traditionally harvested exclusively from the wild, under the name *Yang-tao* – the Strawberry Peach. Wilson had high hopes that this species would become a significant fruit crop in Britain.

The chief disadvantage of this plant, from a gardener's point of view, as a fruit crop, is that the species is dioecious, and therefore a plant of each sex is required to produce fruit. Although bisexual plants do occasionally occur, fruit production is still improved if cross-pollination is possible. When first offered for sale by Veitch the significance of this status was not appreciated. It was not until 1911/12 (when the seedlings first flowered) that it was realised that the great majority of plants were male, and it took some time to locate a female plant. However, the impetus for the development of this plant as a potential fruit crop was quickly lost. This was largely because of the disruptions of the First World War, and the subsequent relocation of many nurseries – and perhaps more significantly, the closure of the Veitch business and the disposal of the stock at the Coombe Wood Nursery. The accelerating decline of the Country House also exacerbated this situation. Both the plants at Heligan, as might be expected, turned out to be male!

Clockwise from top left: The stem and leaves of Actinidia chinensis; *the climber cut back in Winter*

The Chinese Gooseberry is a deciduous, climbing shrub, and can be grown on a relevantly structured framework for fruit production in a suitable climate. It is reasonably hardy, but in the UK it needs the protection of a wall in cold sites to prevent frost damage to the flowers (which are produced in the late Spring). When properly established this plant becomes very vigorous and will need plenty of room. It will require a proper pruning regime if it is to produce fruit and remain in bounds. Our plants continue to grow vigorously, and require a severe annual pruning during the dormant season to keep them under control and in the allotted space. This treatment effectively prevents them from developing flowers, but the large size of the leaves in this vegetative condition makes them extremely decorative.

Araucaria araucana

Araucaria araucana
overlooks the Jungle from the West

Araucaria araucana, the Chilean Pine or Monkey Puzzle, is one of several plants described as 'living fossils' – insofar as this is a tree which dates from the Jurassic period and is virtually unaltered. Fossil remains tell us that not only were there forests of this Araucaria from present-day Brazil to Antarctica, but the distribution probably extended to Britain and Europe.

The Monkey Puzzle is a fairly primitive type of conifer, and today its natural occurrence is limited to three areas of Chile and one area of Argentina – where it is chiefly seen on the Andes at high elevations – very near the tree line, on either side of the border. It is also found as a discrete population along the coastline of Chile – South of the capital, Santiago. In its native habitat logging and habitat incursion have both reduced this tree to endangered status. Sadly, the Bedgebury National Pinetum website says that 'there are now more Monkey Puzzle trees growing in gardens around Britain than in their native country'.

In its native habitat the Monkey Puzzle grows at heights of between 3,000 feet above sea level and the tree line at 6,000 feet. It belongs to the temperate rainforest flora, growing with Southern Beeches (*Nothofagus* spp.) and the Fitzroya. The coastal population of this species is thought to be genetically different from the Andean trees.

This tree is surprisingly tolerant of soil type, as its widespread success in the UK indicates. In Chile it is chiefly found on soils of volcanic origin. It will tolerate salt-laden winds and general maritime exposure, and once it becomes established it is remarkably tolerant of cold – given that the remaining species of Araucaria are all from warm climates and succumb to cold. In the UK, trees will readily reach 65 feet or more in height, with a canopy 36–40 feet wide; however, the tallest trees in their native Chile have been measured at approximately 150 feet.

Monkey Puzzles are dioecious (i.e., they are normally found as single-sex trees); but a few isolated trees in cultivation have produced seed, so it is likely that there are a reasonable number of hermaphrodite trees in the population.

The first European discovery of Araucaria is said to have been *c.*1780 by a Spaniard, Dendoriarena. However, it is Archibald Menzies, the Scottish surgeon/botanist (who was a part of the complement of HMS *Discovery* during the four year-long circumnavigation by Captain George Vancouver) who takes the honours for its introduction to cultivation. It is reputed that, during their stop in Chile, the seeds of the Araucaria were on the table at a banquet given by the

Foliage, cones and bark of Araucaria araucana

Governor (an Irishman), and that Menzies pocketed a few. However, whatever their source, Menzies raised some plants on board ship during the trip – at least one of which, on his return in 1795, was presented to Sir Joseph Banks and planted at Kew. This story has no archival basis to support it, as no reference (apparently) is made in logs, letters or diaries of the captain or crew. The only reference in Menzies' diaries is that he did leave the *Discovery* for an over-land trip to record local plants and collect specimens and seeds – so it is possible he saw the tree. Menzies was obviously a good surgeon as well as a keen and capable botanist, as he was praised by Captain Vancouver for keeping all the crew alive for the duration of the four-year expedition – no mean feat in those days!

The Victorian drive to discover and introduce new plants was enhanced by the employment of plant collectors by nurserymen – one such was the firm of James Veitch & Sons, who over a period of some 60 years sent out 22 plant collectors to all corners of the world. One of the most significant, and the first Veitch collector, was the Cornishman, William Lobb, whose first expedition in 1840 was to South America. He landed in Rio and worked his way across the continent, collecting many exotic and desirable plants, which were dispatched back to Exeter. From his explorations in Chile he sent home a large quantity of Monkey Puzzle seed, which constituted the first major commercial source of the tree for planting. In 1843 Veitch were offering 2-inch tall seedlings at ten shillings for 100 plants. Some customers obviously bought in large quantities, as spectacular avenues were planted at that time.

The best Monkey Puzzles at Heligan are in the Jungle, where four mature specimens high on the skyline have reached 50ft or so. These were no doubt planted after the Great Freeze of April 1891, as any young plants would probably have been killed at that time. The bonus of planting several is that we have both male and female plants, and so occasionally see the production of the huge cones with fertile seed, as is evidenced by the occurrence of self-sown seedlings under the mature trees. We have also planted new trees since the restoration work began.

A stand of original Araucarias in the Jungle

Camellias at Heligan

Camellia japonica *'Eugenie de Massena' on the Western Ride*

John Tremayne is chiefly responsible for planting a remarkable collection of camellias at Heligan. He planted them up the Western Ride, along the top of Beacon Path and down the Eastern Ride. He planted them against the walls of Heligan House and in what came to be called the Italian Garden. He may have inherited some of them from his father, John Hearle Tremayne, because a few of the camellias at Heligan are from the early period of camellia growing in England.

The first living plant in England, a single red, bloomed at the home of Lord Petrie of Thornton Hall, Essex in 1739. It was not until the 1790s that camellias came into the country in any numbers, and these were mostly not wild ones, but garden varieties introduced from gardens and nurseries of China. Their introduction was linked to the growing tea trade with China through the HEIC. It is said that these decorative camellias were often substituted for the tea camellia, *Camellia sinensis*, to try to prevent the valuable tea plants from leaving China, but John Reeves, responsible for the collection of many specimens sent to England, was the company's Chief Inspector of Tea and unlikely to have been fooled.

The plants were brought to England by sailing ship. The voyage took up to a year and, given the vagaries of travelling through the tropics and around the Cape of Good Hope, it is remarkable that any survived. Captain Corner of the East Indiaman *Carnatic* brought in the first variety in 1792. This was *Camellia japonica* 'Alba Plena', a beautiful white double. By 1824 a dozen or more different varieties had arrived, including the famous *Camellia reticulata* 'Captain Rawes', brought back by Richard Rawes, captain of the East Indiaman *Warren Hastings*. This deep pink camellia was eventually named after him, so assuring him of his place in horticultural history.

These exotic plants were imported first as highly desirable presents for friends and family, but increasingly at the request of commercial nurseries or of the recently formed London Horticultural Society (later the Royal Horticultural Society). As a member of the Society, John Hearle would have seen these early introductions, perhaps taking time off from his duties in the House of Commons to visit the most famous collection of the day at Chiswick House, home of the Duke of Devonshire, and at the Society's gardens next door.

He may have had access to the plants themselves and, although until the second half of the century camellias were generally considered too tender to be planted outside, Cornwall was noted for the clemency of its climate, and it is likely that camellias were being grown in the open; certainly this appears to have been so at nearby Tregothnan.

At Heligan, there were, until recently, three early varieties that may have survived from John Hearle's time:

- *Camellia japonica* 'Fimbriata'. This is a sport of 'Alba Plena' that was imported from China in 1816 for the Colville Nursery in the King's Road, Chelsea. This camellia leans over the rocky path at the top of the Ravine. It has beautiful white flowers whose evenly-arranged petals show a delicate fringing.
- *C. japonica* 'Althaeiflora', later renamed 'Blackburniana'. This was a chance seedling from *C. japonica* 'Anemoniflora' raised by Chandlers of Vauxhall in 1819. Our tree is flourishing; the leaves on some limbs are mottled and blotched with yellow, the tell-tale symptom of the camellia

Clockwise from top left: Camellia japonica *'Blackburniana',* C. japonica *'Gloire de Nantes',* C. japonica *'Lavinia Maggi', and* C. japonica *'Archiduchesse Marie'*

leaf virus, but the unaffected leaves are deep green and lustrous. Its large anemone-shaped flowers are deep, pure red. This camellia stands on the Western Ride near the Garden entrance.

- *C. reticulata* 'Captain Rawes'. At one time there were two of this variety planted in the protection of the outside walls of the Flower Garden. The larger, which according to an 1896 report 'bears hundreds of huge flowers annually', was planted against the north wall, a hollow wall warmed by heat from the boiler flue. This camellia was lost in 1963. The other 'Captain Rawes' was planted on the west wall of the Flower Garden in Sikkim. It became choked by rhododendrons and, although it bore a few leaves and the odd flower until recently, it died in 2004.

The origin of many of the camellias planted later by John Tremayne has, for many years, been a mystery. It is now thought that these are part of a collection of continental camellias, many of them characterised by a white stripe down the centre of each petal. Recent investigations have tried to name more of this unique collection, many of which seem to be extremely rare. The search led from camellia collections in Cornwall to the shores of the Italian lakes; from hand-coloured nursery catalogues of the 1820s to tattered nursery stock lists of the 1880s.

A set of rare books, 12 volumes dating from 1848 to 1860, provided the clues to Heligan's collection. These were the catalogues of the famous Verschaffelt Nursery of Ghent and they contained illustrations and descriptions of the camellias that the nursery offered for sale. Here at last were pictures of varieties like the ones at Heligan. By comparing these illustrations with our living plants, and researching contemporary literature for the varieties available in England at the time, some possible identifications have been made.

Along the Western Ride and in the Italian Garden are several examples of the early-flowering 'Gloire de Nantes'. Towards the bottom of the Western Ride is a fine, striped camellia that fits the description for 'Archiduchesse Marie'. Close by is the lovely 'Eugenie de Massena'. On Flora's Green, just outside the Vegetable Garden is 'Arciduchessa Augusta'; the pink one, which reaches from the edge of the grass to Western Ride, is probably 'Mathotiana Rosea'. On Beacon Path is an early example of 'Lavinia Maggi', a formal double with white flowers streaked with carmine and red. In the Jungle is a veteran specimen of 'Donckelaeri', a semi-double, its deep-red flowers marbled with white.

The search to name more of these lovely old plants continues.

Camellia reticulata 'Captain Rawes'

Camellia reticulata *'Captain Rawes' on the south wall of the Flower Garden*

The nineteenth century was the century of 'plant fever' in Britain. Beautiful and unusual exotic plants were filling the important British gardens and providing satisfaction for their wealthy owners. The plant hunters were scouring the world to satisfy this demand, often enduring considerable hardship and even losing their lives, but achieving national hero status.

As far as this particular story is concerned, it is the year 1820, and Richard Rawes, Captain of the HEIC's ship *Warren Hastings*, has returned from China with a plant of a brand new, unnamed camellia, which probably had been obtained from the famous Fa-Te nurseries in Canton. This he gave as a present to a relative, Thomas Carey Palmer of Bromley in Kent, who owned a conservatory – as it was believed generally that camellias were not hardy and needed such protection.

There the plant continued to grow happily, and in the late Spring of 1826 it bloomed for the first time. Its incredible, large (about 4ins across), semi-double, bright carmine flowers expanded, and it was hailed as one of the most beautiful camellias ever seen.

Clearly it was quite distinct from *Camellia japonica* – which by this time was well known in Britain. As it presented several very distinct characteristics, the botanist John Lindley, writing in the *Botanical Register*, recognised it as a separate species and named it *C. reticulata* – from the very evident pattern of veins on the leaf. This variety was named in honour of Captain Rawes, and was thus the very first of this species to be brought to the West. It remained the only example of the species in the country until 20 years later, when Robert Fortune introduced a second variety with double red blooms, which was named 'Robert Fortune'.

Initially, in both Britain and America these two varieties proved more difficult to grow than *Camellia japonica* – in the ground and in greenhouses. They were relatively difficult to propagate from cuttings, and were not compatible with the usual *C. sasanqua* rootstocks used in grafting.

The public loved these camellias because of their splendid flowers, with bigger size and typically ruffled and swirled petals, in bright tones of pinks and reds (a glowing carmine in 'Captain Rawes'). Also, they flowered later than *Camellia japonica*, so avoiding the worst of the weather. Thus attempts were made to cross them with various *japonica* varieties to create hybrids which were easier to grow and had a midway flowering period – but with very limited success. *C. reticulata* eventually proved to be more compatible with *C. saluenensis*, and several good hybrids were produced.

The story of *Camellia reticulata* 'Captain Rawes' has a final twist. *C. reticulata* had been selected and cultivated only in the Temple Gardens of Yunnan ever since the Ming Dynasty. The Kunming Historical Institute of Yunnan gathered together all the *reticulata* camellias that could be found in the area. There were more than 100, but strangely this particular camellia was not among them. Because it had proved so difficult to propagate, it had apparently died out in the land of its birth. So, when it was brought back to China from an American Nursery, it was welcomed with joy and received the name 'Guixia', which means 'Returning Cloud'.

Camellia reticulata 'Captain Rawes' has been grown here at Heligan since mid-Victorian times. Until relatively recently there was a fine specimen which had been planted and trained on the north-facing 'flued' wall of the Flower Garden, just to the West of the big door. This succeeded extraordinarily well, and grew so tall that the wall was extended upwards to accommodate and protect it. It flowered profusely each year, with literally hundreds of blooms, until it was blown down in a storm in 1963 and died. There is a fine photograph of Commander and Mrs Thomas, who were then the tenants of Heligan, posing in front of the tree. Another specimen had been planted, at much the same time, on the outside of the west wall of the Flower Garden, facing Sikkim. This plant was still alive (just) in the 1990s – its head poking up over the wall, and a few flowers were produced each year, which could be seen from inside the Flower Garden. It finally succumbed in 2004.

However, *Camellia reticulata* 'Captain Rawes' is still to be found in the Gardens, as we planted several young trees on the south wall of the Flower Garden in 1997. These are being fan-trained, and are flowering already, producing their magnificent flowers in very acceptable numbers. They are there to provide cut flowers. In Victorian and Edwardian times, cut flowers of all descriptions were required to decorate the House, and these beautiful blossoms were often used on the dinner table where they would be floated on water in ornate bowls.

A young, fan-trained plant (top).
Leaves and buds of Camellia reticulata *'Captain Rawes' (above)*

Cornus capitata

Anecdotal evidence indicates that this most attractive, but somewhat tender Flowering Dogwood was first introduced to cultivation, in this country, at Heligan. It is reputed that a local Member of Parliament, Sir Anthony Buller (MP for Liskeard), having made an expedition to Nepal, returned in 1825 with seeds of this plant (then called *Benthamia fragifera*) and presented them to his fellow MP and friend, John Hearle Tremayne of Heligan.

This small tree belongs to the 'Dogwood' genus (*Cornus*), which is best known for the more commonly encountered species of familiar, coloured-bark, shrubby Dogwoods. The Himalayan Strawberry Tree, however, is one of that group of species described as the 'Flowering Dogwoods'. Also in this group are the more widely known, Eastern Asiatic, *Cornus kousa*, *C. florida* from the South East of North America, and *C. nuttallii* from the West Coast.

All of this particular group of species have the same type of unusually structured inflorescences in which a small, hemispherical mass of inconspicuous, true flowers are subtended by substantially sized and colourful bracts.

This species was introduced from Nepal; but presumably from the lower slopes of the Himalaya, as it is only marginally hardy. It is also native to South Western China, and has since been introduced from here too. Consequently, it is only found growing satisfactorily in cultivation in the milder parts of the South of the UK, and in other similarly mild niches. It grows most successfully and luxuriantly here in the far South West, and it is undoubtedly seen at its best in Cornish gardens – especially in those mild valley gardens close to the South Coast. Here the mild, moist conditions seem to suit it very well. It also grows particularly well in South Western Ireland. Soil type does not seem to affect performance significantly, although under alkaline soil conditions it may not be so vigorous.

It is an extremely fast-growing plant, and flowers early in its life (around the fourth year), when it is also capable of developing prolific quantities of viable seed. This characteristic allowed Squire John Hearle Tremayne to line the new Long Drive to the House,

A replacement Cornus capitata *on the original Long Drive to Heligan House (top). A tree on Flora's Green (above)*

on its completion in 1832, with this tree (only seven years after its introduction) – a task that required 400 plants.

Only one tree remains from this original introduction – that on the north edge of Flora's Green, where a number of seedlings were re-introduced in the early 1990s. At the start of the restoration, the Long Drive to Heligan House was also replanted, and some of these plants have already become sizeable trees, visible from the new crossing into the Gardens.

The tree has the potential to grow to a height of 50ft, and if grown in an open situation will usually become multi-stemmed, and can spread to as much as 70ft. Here at Heligan we have recently planted many individuals throughout the Gardens – where they have usually been in fairly crowded situations. Under these conditions the trees grow erect to some 16–20ft in eight years, and with more or less a single stem. The trees have generally produced flowers and fruits with viable seeds when as young as four years old – and when they are little more than 8ft tall.

The light green leaves are broadly elliptic in shape, and generally some 3ins in length, exhibiting a dull, greyish sheen for most of the year. Autumn leaf colour is not spectacular but is usually a bright, butter-yellow in a dry season. The plant varies from nearly evergreen to deciduous, according to its exposure to cold temperatures. The foliage is remarkably tolerant of the salt carried by winds off the sea.

Depending on the earliness of the season, flowering begins from the end of May or the beginning of June, and is prolific – the colourful bracts persisting for several weeks. The 'flowers' are decorative because of the (more or less) five colourful, wide and substantial bracts which subtend the flower. These 'flowers' are about 3 inches across, and the bracts are bright, sulphur yellow, although in any population of seedlings some vary towards butter yellow. As the flowers age, the bracts develop attractive red and pink longitudinal streaks.

The decorative fruits are fleshy and unshapely. They look something between a strawberry and a lychee, and consist of an amorphous, orange-fleshed mass with an orange-red skin which matures to a red-purple. The fruit can be up to 2 inches in diameter, and many seeds are embedded in the flesh. The flesh is particularly sought out by birds.

From top: A flower, mature flowers and fruit of Cornus capitata

The species was granted an Award of Merit (AM) when shown to the Royal Horticultural Society in 1922.

Crinodendron hookerianum

Crinodendron hookerianum *in the Jungle*

The Chilean Lantern Tree is the derived European common name for *Crinodendron hookerianum* (which is found in early texts as *Tricuspidaria lanceolata*). This evergreen shrub, of twiggy habit, with very dark green willow-shaped leaves, produces from each leaf axil a single, hanging, globe-shaped, red to rosy pink flower on a long stalk – in which the petals split and open to develop a bell- or lantern-shaped form. Once established, it grows into a large, spreading shrub, which will flower prolifically and create a remarkable sight. It will also flower quite adequately on smaller plants, and even on nursery-sized plants.

It is a native of the temperate rainforest region of Southern Chile and was found and introduced to Britain, in 1848, by one of Cornwall's most famous professional plant collectors of the Victorian era – William Lobb. At that time he was on his first collecting trip – travelling and collecting for Messrs James Veitch & Sons of Exeter, in Central and South America.

Although this plant will tolerate a limited degree of frost and cold temperature, it flourishes best in mild climates such as those experienced here in the sheltered coastal areas of the far South West – where the incidence of cold is much diminished. Its temperate rainforest provenance is not dissimilar to the climate of Cornwall, which would itself climax in a similar type of vegetation if allowed to mature. Thus it would normally expect to flourish here, and the environment at Heligan seems to suit it particularly well.

At Heligan this shrub was obviously originally planted in several places, as groups of old plants have survived (despite having become overgrown and generally in poor condition) both at the back of Flora's Green and in the Jungle. These plantings have reached about 20 feet in height – which seems to be the maximum it will achieve, as, at this level, it tends to die off and then regenerate from low down in the crown. This has produced (in these untended plants) a straggling and spreading mass of fairly upright, insubstantial branches which carry little foliage low down.

Because of this habit of regularly dying back, it is difficult to estimate the age of our plants, but it is safe to assume, by deduction and from contemporary evidence, that they were present at least by the mid-1890s.

Clockwise from top: A squirrel in the Crinodendron; the lantern-like flowers; suckers regenerate from an original plant

Crinodendron hookerianum appears to flourish best in conditions where it is not exposed to continuous full sun all day long. In the forest understorey, in glades and forest edges, it would be shaded for part of the day. As would be expected of a rainforest plant, it succeeds best in an organic soil, and one which is reasonably acidic. Soils in such climates become substantially leached – removing the soluble calcareous compounds and becoming acidic – a feature that is also typical of soils in Cornwall.

Crinodendron hookerianum initially develops as an upright, branching shrub, with a thicket-like habit, which grows quickly and vigorously when young. As the older branches pass maturity they tend to die off, and are replaced by stems from low on the plant. It has the potential to grow into a substantially sized shrub if left unchecked. Extensive replanting has taken place in a grove-like situation on either side of the Boardwalk to the West of Third Pond in the Jungle. After seven years of maturing, it now produces a remarkable show annually.

The leaves are lanceolate, dark green above and silvery blue beneath, somewhat leathery in texture and normally about 3 inches long, just less than an inch in width, and toothed on the margins. It is evergreen.

It flowers profusely in May and June, for a three- to four-week period, and at Heligan is invariably a spectacular sight, always attracting notice and interest. Small numbers of flowers are also produced sporadically into the late Summer.

The individual flowers are globular and about an inch across, with a 2-ins long, drooping stalk; all the parts – petals, sepals and flower stalk – are completely red and hang down like red lanterns – one in each leaf axil of last year's growth. There are five petals which form an inverted globose but narrow-mouthed lantern in which the petals eventually split. The three sepals are short, the same colour, and sit on top of the lantern. These flowers are unusual in that the developed buds are produced in the Autumn, but do not open until early Summer the following year.

Davidia involucrata

The Pocket Handkerchief Tree in the Sundial Garden (above). A view from beneath the Tree; the bracts with true flowers, and fruits with leaf-buds (right)

This unusual tree, from the western parts of Szechwan and Hupeh in China, is known by a number of vernacular names in the UK – Dove Tree, Pocket Handkerchief Tree and Ghost Tree – all of which allude to the large white 'flowers' which are produced prolifically on mature trees.

This tree was first observed and described for the West by Père Armand David, in 1869, and was seen subsequently by several others. All who had seen it extolled the beauty and interest of its flowers, and even the Keeper of the Herbarium at Kew wrote (when writing about the plant in Hooker's *Icones Plantarum* in 1891) that 'Davidia is a tree almost deserving a special mission to western China with a view to its introduction to European gardens'. Thus the race was on to locate and introduce it, and eventually a special mission was what it got!

In the Spring of 1899, E.H. Wilson was commissioned by Messrs Veitch to undertake an expedition to China on their behalf, with his primary remit being to find the Davidia, collect seed and expedite its dispatch to Britain. Success in this venture would continue to confirm the reputation of the House of Veitch as a premier collector and introducer of 'exotic' plants to Europe. In this Wilson succeeded – sending back large quantities of fruits, which arrived in Britain in the Spring of 1901. However, unknown to Wilson (and to Veitch at the time of his departure), in 1897 a French missionary, Père Farges, had dispatched a packet of 37 fruits to M. Maurice de Vilmorin in France. In June 1899 one only of these germinated – which proved to be the sum total of success – but the race was over and the French had won.

Various techniques of germination were employed on Wilson's large consignment of seeds by the propagator at Veitch's Nursery at Coombe Wood. It was the particular sample which was sown early and left outside to experience the warmth of a Summer followed by the cold of a Winter that succeeded best. In the Spring of 1902 Messrs Veitch were able to pot up some 13,000 seedling trees. Despite having lost the race to the French, this overwhelming success laid the basis of a commercial coup, and was responsible for the vast majority of trees of this species which were in cultivation during the first half of the twentieth century.

These seedling trees were first distributed by Veitch in about 1905, and it is assumed that the Heligan tree is one of these – other plants in the Garden indicate that Jack Tremayne bought in a batch of (newly introduced) plants at about that period (cf. *Actinidia* in the Italian Garden). The tree is standing at the head of the Sundial Garden, and is planted a few feet in from the far, west-facing wall.

The characteristic ornamental feature of this tree is the 'flower'. As might be expected of a plant ancestrally related to a group of plants which include Cornus, the true flowers are relatively insignificant and are carried in a bunch, just less than an inch in diameter, on the end of a 3-ins stalk; however they are subtended by extraordinarily beautiful and ornamental bracts. There are usually two of these bracts – one below and one above the flower cluster. They are large, substantial, somewhat oblong, just about dished and with a long point. The lower bract is usually about 6ins long and half as wide, and the upper bract is about half the size and stands over the flowers as a hood – eventually flopping downwards. Both are clear white, although they have a greenish tinge when fresh.

The Heligan tree, like many others in Cornwall, has become multiple-stemmed – although trees further up country are often single-stemmed, tall (easily reaching 60–70ft in semi-woodland situations), and pyramidal in shape. Our tree seems to continually renew itself from very strong 'watershoots', which arise from near the base of tall stems that have 'shown their head above the parapet' and are beginning to die back. Overall it barely exceeds 20ft in height.

The flowers are produced in May and last for three to four weeks. The cluster of true flowers consists of numerous male flowers and one perfect flower. Flower production is invariably prolific, and the slightest breeze causes the bracts to ripple and flutter – making the whole tree appear to be loaded with huge white butterflies, white doves or even handkerchiefs – depending on your imagination! It first flowered at Coombe Wood in 1911, and was awarded a First Class Certificate (FCC) by the RHS in 1911.

The leaves are bright, mid-green and broadly oval in shape with a heart-shaped base and the tip drawn into a long point. Overall they are about 4ins long and 3ins at their broadest. The margins of the leaves are coarsely toothed with triangular indentations, and the blades are characterised by usually eight prominent pairs of more or less parallel veins, and the leaf stalk is 2ins long. Autumn colour is not a strong point in our climate.

The fruits are about the size of a small walnut. They have a gritty flesh and a thick skin which ripens from green to brown; internally there is a nut which consists of about five linear segments, each containing a seed. The fruits tend to remain hanging from the branches right into the New Year. The Davidia first fruited in the UK in 1915.

Davidia is sufficiently unlike any other plant growing today that it is accorded its own family with a single genus and the one (maybe two) species.

Dicksonia antarctica

Dicksonia antarctica *in the Jungle*

The sunlight filtered down through the massive fronds above me. This was my first introduction to Heligan's Tree Ferns; although in 1969, at the age of twelve, I didn't know what they were. I used to come with other children from the nearby fishing village of Mevagissey to play in what we called 'The Jungle'. This was when Heligan was still truly lost – not to be rediscovered for another 20 years. I thought these were beautiful plants, almost prehistoric, and well worth fighting our way through the wild bamboo and overgrown rhododendrons which in some places totally blocked out the sky, creating black tunnels under their twisting, interwoven boughs. We used the fronds to make roofs for our camps, and occasionally dragged one home to keep – although they usually wilted and died in a couple of days.

These original Heligan Tree Ferns are an Australian species, *Dicksonia antarctica*, named in honour of James Dickson, a founder member of the London Horticultural Society. It is a slow-growing species, which in its native habitat can develop a trunk up to 40ft tall, with fronds up to 13ft long. A new crop of fronds develops each Spring from the top of the trunk, and the old fronds slowly die off, hanging down to form a skirt around the gradually rising trunk – eventually rotting off. The new fronds, with their delicate fiddleback appearance as they unfold, are also a delight. It is difficult to determine the age of a Tree Fern as it has no annual rings or other indicators. Technically the trunk is a rhizome with adventitious roots, whose main purpose is to stabilise the plant.

Various stories have been told about how these Tree Ferns arrived in Cornwall – some (in the latter half of the nineteenth century) were possibly used as ballast in ships returning from Australia. However, the majority of the Tree Ferns which abound in the larger gardens in Cornwall and are certainly of pre-Great War vintage, derived from the efforts of John Garland Treseder, who had emigrated from Truro to Australia in the 1870s, and established a nursery at Paramatta in New South Wales. Over some two decades from 1892 onwards, he sent literally hundreds of dry trunks directly to various estate owners in Cornwall, and latterly to the re-established Treseder Nursery at Moresk. These importations continued up until 1914. The trunks arrived, by ship, at Falmouth and (so legend has it) were off-loaded on to railway trucks, which transported them to Truro and then along the viaduct to just above Moresk, where they were heaved over the parapet and dropped into the stream that ran beside the Nursery. Here they remained until they had soaked up enough water to rehydrate, and begin the process of expanding new fronds during the next Spring. In the early years of the twentieth century they were a regular item in the Treseder catalogues.

The environment throughout Heligan, and especially in the Jungle, is ideal for the growth of these ferns, as the Gardens are on the whole sheltered, warm, humid, and with reasonable tree cover. This Tree Fern (with the Chusan Palm) was evidently part of Jack Tremayne's vision as a structural plant in the Jungle – as indicated by their sheer number in the valley bottom. During his time as Squire many new plants suitable only for the mild Cornish climate were arriving in Britain. Jack realised that those which would otherwise require greenhouse treatment, could survive here out of doors. He wanted to use the part of Heligan that ran down the valley towards Mevagissey as the site for his Jungle mixture of Bamboo, Rhododendron, Gunnera, Palms, Tree Ferns and other exotica: it was sheltered from high winds and had its own unique, mild and moist micro-climate. This Jungle would be a mix of wild, natural plants and overseas exotics – so pushing gardening fashion to the extremes. Although these Tree Ferns are about the hardiest of the available species, it is still a plant that is susceptible to cold, and especially to late spring frost (which will severely damage the newly emerging fronds), and hence it is prudent to protect the crown during the Winter.

Sunlight filters through the fronds of Dicksonia antarctica *(top); the moose specimen in the Jungle (above)*

Tree Ferns are a major feature of the garden landscape at Heligan – there are well over 120 which have survived from the original plantings – and these have been gapped up and added to with about another 50 or more from an importation from Tasmania in the early 1990s, which were planted throughout the Gardens, and are also an integral part of plantings around the Crystal Grotto and New Zealand.

There are fossils of the earliest *Dicksonia antarctica* which date back to the Jurassic period, making this a truly prehistoric plant. Looking at them today, with their massive, moss-covered trunks, it is easy to be transported back in time.

Look carefully at the ferns in the middle of the Jungle, and you will see one that has started to fall over and has then righted itself by upward growth. Where this has happened, the trunk folds and sags, and now looks like the neck of a huge old moose. In fact each Tree Fern seems to have its own personality.

Tree Ferns in the Jungle in Winter

Drimys winteri

Drimys winteri
on the Eastern Ride

It is easy to forget, when looking at a particular plant, that beyond the beauty of the leaf or flower, there often lies a fascinating story of how the plant itself came into cultivation in our gardens. The story of *Drimys winteri*, from the temperate rainforests of the southern tip of South America, is one such plant. The tale of its discovery and introduction begins more than 400 years ago.

In 1577, Captain-General Francis Drake set sail from Plymouth Sound in his ship *The Pelican* (later the *Golden Hind*) on a circumnavigation of the Globe. Accompanying him on his three-year trip were two other ships – one of which, the *Elizabeth*, was under the command of an intelligent and capable 22-year-old, Captain John Winter. Initially they set sail for the Straits of Magellan, and eventually arrived there after eleven arduous months of tedium and damaging storms – but capturing several ships and plundering much cargo *en route*.

During the voyage, the natural history of the regions visited was recorded and sampled. It is possible that *Drimys winteri* was first given to Captain Winter by the native Indians on the coast of *Terra Magellanica*, who used it as a symbol of peace. Perhaps by observing the practices of these indigenous peoples, he also came to understand that the plant had curative properties, as they used it against dyspepsia, nausea, colic and asthma. Captain Winter is said to have chewed the peppery-tasting bark to cure his own stomach upset, and when used by his crew it was discovered that it alleviated scurvy. This significant and widespread problem of sailors on long voyages was a debilitating and disfiguring disease which caused blackened gums and loose teeth, blotched limbs, stiff joints, depression and mental aberrations. Scurvy is caused chiefly by a deficiency of Vitamin C in the diet, and the bark of *D. winteri* has since proved to be a rich source of this vitamin. As a result of this discovery, the plant became known as Winter's Bark, or sometimes Pepper Bark because of its taste.

Some 200 years after Drake, another famous explorer was setting out on his second circumnavigation. In 1772 Captain James Cook took charge of the *Resolution* for a three-year voyage to the South Seas. On board were Johann Reinhold Forster and his son George, who were replacing Sir Joseph Banks (who had been on the first trip) as naturalists – Banks had declined to make the trip as the ship could not be converted to his requirements without considerable expense. The Forsters were appointed 'at the King's pleasure' as naturalists to the expedition, and subsequently recorded their discoveries and observations in two volumes. George's *A Voyage round the World in His Britannic Majesty's Sloop Resolution* was published in 1777, and Rheinhold's *Observations made during a Voyage round the World* in 1778. It is to these two scholars that the classification and naming of *Drimys winteri* can be attributed. Later William Woodville, a noted physician and botanist of the time, understood the value of Forster's introduction, and included the plant in his publication *Medical Botany* of 1790.

Drimys winteri was originally cultivated for its medicinal value, but it has proved to be a wonderful plant for those gardens with some shelter, and which are not particularly cold (it can be considerably harmed by late-winter or spring frost). An evergreen tree, it is native to the southernmost parts of Chile and Argentina, where it grows in temperate rainforests with Nothofagus, Saxegothaea and Podocarpus. In its natural habitat it grows quickly to over 50 ft, but our biggest example is only half that size. The leaves are long and linear – up to about 8 inches long; they are leathery, and an attractive glossy green with a whitish bloom on the underside. The bark is a pale green colour on Heligan's conventional, old introduction (on Eastern Ride); but we now have seedlings from new introductions of Chilean seed with brown, 'red' and yellow-green bark. Our plants flower prolifically from late Winter into Spring, producing umbels of jasmine-scented, ivory-white, one-inch-diameter flowers with a central boss of yellow stamens. Overall the effect is very handsome, and the newer trees in the garden of the Steward's House always receive lots of attention from visitors, despite the competition from rhododendrons, camellias and the early bulbs. *Drimys winteri* is a plant that clearly enjoys our Atlantic temperate rainforest climate and, provided it receives protection from the worst of the easterly winds, it flourishes. It grows best in moist, lime-free soil. Once established in a suitable position it will grow quickly, needing little or no further pruning or management.

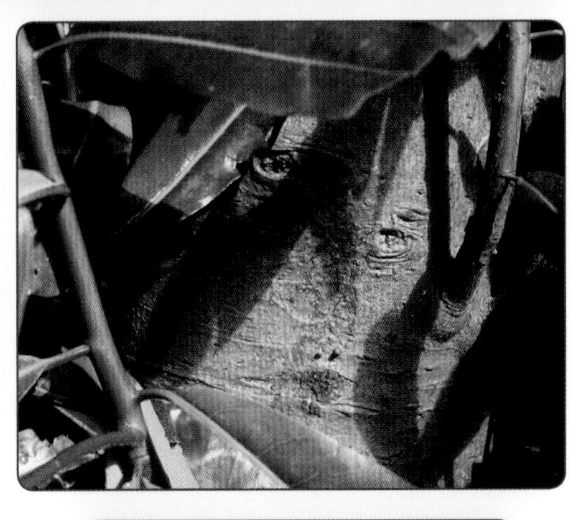

The flowers, trunk, berries and leaves of Drimys winteri

I find it impossible to look at this beautiful and impressive plant without conjuring up images of the early exploration of the South American coasts, violent storms at Cape Horn, and sailors tragically disfigured by the effects of scurvy.

Eucryphia cordifolia

Eucryphia cordifolia *down the Eastern Ride*

Eucryphia cordifolia is an evergreen shrub from the temperate rainforests of Chile. In Cornwall, with its similarly mild, humid climate, it will mature into a stately, columnar tree, often growing to some 40ft high. Indeed, the tallest recorded specimen in the Country is down the road from Heligan at Tregrehan: it is about 60ft tall.

The Heligan specimen stands in the Northern Gardens, about three-quarters of the way down the Eastern Ride on the seaward side. It is 35–40ft high, broadly columnar in shape, and clothed with branches to the ground. It is a sturdy feature in the landscape, which puts on a spectacular show when it produces a myriad of white blossoms in August through to early September.

This Eucryphia does not have any English common name, but is called *Ulmo* or *Muermo* locally. It is native to the lower levels of the Andean slopes in both Chile and Argentina. In Chile it is found on the island of Chiloe, and in the central provinces of Valdivia and Lianquihue – areas of relatively high rainfall. This creates the environment for the plant-rich, temperate rainforest. Nowadays these areas are dramatically under threat from both logging and papermaking, and this Eucryphia, although not yet endangered, is certainly at risk. In the wild it is an integral part of the various temperate rainforest ecosystems of the Chilean coastal ranges. These are dominated by large conifers such as Fitzroya, Saxegothea and various Podocarpus, which intersperse with the Southern Beeches (*Nothofagus*); in the understorey are, typically, not only the Eucryphia but also shrubs such as Drimys and Embothrium; the bamboo Chusquea; the climber *Lapageria rosea*, and the hard fern Blechnum – a veritable gardener's treasure trove.

The leaves of this evergreen tree are long-lived. They are broadly oblong and wavy edged, dark green and leathery, with a shiny upper surface and downy underside. On a mature plant the leaf blades are usually about 3ins long, and just over an inch wide, with a short stalk leading to a heart-shaped leaf base. On a young plant the leaves tend to be narrower and serrated.

In Cornwall the tree flowers in August and early September, with white, rose-like blooms similar to those of a Rose of Sharon, and they are scented. The single flowers are about 2ins across, and have four white, spreading petals which are backed by fire-coloured sepals. The white petals surround a central boss of yellow carpels, and a mass of conspicuous brown stamens which create a contrast at the heart of each blossom. The flowers are produced in the leaf axils near the tips of the branches. This spectacular, late-season flowering habit makes this genus of tree-scale plants very valuable in a garden. The flowers are pollinated by bees, and the honey is much sought after. In general, a mature tree is host to a wide variety of wild life.

As this is a shrub which is typical of the protected environment of the understorey of a temperate rainforest, it is not surprising that it does not tolerate wind or frost well – unless it is suitably protected by surrounding vegetation, and preferably by overhanging trees. The species appears to be fairly tolerant of soil types, but would probably prefer to grow in a reasonably acid soil with a high organic-matter content.

The bark of this species is rich in tannins and was used locally for tanning. The wood is red-coloured, heavy, strong, hard, close-grained and durable. It is used in general construction, for furniture and flooring, and was especially prized for the manufacture of oars. In the construction of the railways it was particularly regarded for the production of railway sleepers. It also makes good charcoal. All in all, the Eucryphia is a valuable resource, and a decorative, late-summer-flowering shrub.

Buds and leaves, and the rose-like flowers of Eucryphia cordifolia

The Heligan tree was probably planted in the 1890s, on the return of Jack Tremayne from Italy. He obviously set about updating many parts of the Garden for his elderly father – a programme which also involved new features. The borders on the Eastern Ride contained many mature camellias (some of which are still present); but the presence of the *Podocarpus salignus* at the top end of the Ride (towards the Northern Summerhouse); the avenue of Trachycarpus palms, and the Eucryphia and evergreen Azaleas (at that lower end) all suggest that a major revamp of the area was undertaken somewhere about this time. This tree is also a Veitch introduction, and we know that Jack was purchasing plants from them extensively.

Ginkgo biloba

The Ginkgo biloba *on Eastern Ride seen from the Vegetable Garden (above). The foliage in Summer (left) and Autumn (below left)*

This only surviving species of an ancient plant group – the Ginkgophyta – *Ginkgo biloba* is known to have survived on earth for over 150 million years, making this incredible prehistoric survivor the oldest living tree. During that time it had a distribution across most of the Northern Hemisphere, including what has become the British Isles. Appropriately, it was Charles Darwin who, in 1859, referred to the Ginkgo as a 'living fossil', and amazingly it was the very first plant to flower in Hiroshima after the atomic bomb.

The Ginkgo is a native of China. This deciduous conifer, having survived the Ice Age, has been cultivated in temples by Chinese Buddhist monks (who considered the tree to be sacred), and in the grounds of royal palaces for many centuries. It was generally cultivated for its wood and medicinal properties. It is doubtful if it grows anywhere, nowadays, in a truly wild state.

Surveys conducted in China have revealed that a few trees are as much as 3,000 years old, and about 150 trees exceed 500 years old. In approximately AD 800 the Ginkgo spread to Japan, and then continued to spread through Eastern Asia – usually as a sacred or revered tree, generally planted by Buddhists in temple gardens. It was made known to Europeans *c.*1692, from Japan, having been seen by the German physician and botanist, Engelbert Kaempfer, during his epic trip to the Far East for the Dutch East India Company. It was Kaempfer who gave it the name Maidenhair Tree, because of the similar shape of the leaves to the local Maidenhair Fern. Eventually, in 1730, seeds arrived at the Botanic Garden at Utrecht, and trees found their way to England in 1754. The Royal Garden at Kew was one of the first proud recipients, and its tree still stands as a relatively young specimen of 250 years old.

Although sadly the Ginkgo is generally considered extinct in wild areas, it continues to thrive in temples and gardens and, thanks to its amazing survival techniques and ability to tolerate environmental pollution, throughout urban landscapes across the world.

The Victorian fascination with new and interesting plants is surely the reason for the tree being present in the Gardens at Heligan. Thanks to Squire John Tremayne, two can be found in the Jungle, and one stands towering above the Eastern Ride opposite New Zealand. All three of these specimens were probably planted in the 1870s and, according to reports, were possibly grown from seed obtained from Kew.

Although most flowering plants have both male and female reproductive parts, the Ginkgo is dioecious. The trees here at Heligan are all of a fastigiate (upright) habit, and this seems to be connected with their being male.

Therefore, Heligan does not bear witness to the fruits of this ancient species, which themselves give this amazing tree the first part of its name. *Ginkgo* (in Chinese *Gin-kyo*) translates as 'Silver Apricot', which describes the fleshy fruits of the female trees; while *biloba* is the Latin for two-lobed – referring to the unique and distinctive shape of the leaf.

The Ginkgo in Summer

Surprisingly, the smell of the ripening fruits can be quite unpleasant. Often abundantly produced, the fleshy fruits fall in October, when they have a nauseous odour similar to that of rancid butter, due to the presence of butyric acid. Additionally, the pulp can cause an allergic reaction for some people, and consequently only male trees are recommended for urban landscape use.

Ginkgo today is widely recognised and renowned for its medicinal properties. Extracts are used worldwide to treat a variety of ailments from asthma to circulatory problems, and even Alzheimer's disease.

Although the age and evolutionary position of the Ginkgo is now well understood, even in ancient times it was revered and regarded as sacred among trees. Maybe it is the way that it blooms at night, shedding its blossoms promptly in relative secrecy, that has accredited it with mystical powers. Daoist shamans even used to carve their magical spells on ancient Ginkgo wood, in order to communicate with the spirit world.

Whether you know it as the Ancestor Tree, Buddha's Fingernail Tree, Maidenhair Tree or simply the Ginkgo, it is evident that these incredible trees really are one of the planet's greatest survivors. So next time you pass one of these unique 'old souls' of the tree world, take a few moments to admire its beauty, structure and presence and contemplate its amazing evolution. Who knows, with its unique ability to withstand pollution and survive exposure to harmful radiation, the Ginkgo, along with the cockroach, may just outlive us humans!

Hoheria sexstylosa

The old Hoheria sexstylosa *in Sikkim*

Although there is only one of the original trees of this Hoheria species left in the Gardens (in Sikkim, behind the Flower Garden wall), we have a host of its progeny, especially in the Steward's House Garden and around the Ticket Office. They become quite a feature in the summer, smothered with their beautiful delicate flowers. This small tree sets seeds prolifically, and these germinate readily. So it has almost become a weed.

Hoheria sexstylosa is a small, very elegant, evergreen tree. There is a specimen in New Zealand by the Maori Hut – where this young tree has already reached about 10ft in height – and there are several good-looking trees in the garden of the Steward's House – a couple of which have already reached 20ft in only ten years or so. All of these trees look spectacular in August, when they are almost completely covered in a mass of smallish, white flowers.

Hoheria sexstylosa is a native of New Zealand, and is one of some five species of the genus. The Maori name for this tree is *Houiongaonga* (please don't ask how to pronounce it!) or *Houhere* – from which is derived its generic name. The common name for all the species is Ribbonwood or Lacebark, which refers to the lace-like fronds behind the bark. This species is known as the Long-leaved Lacebark.

The inner bark is edible, but was only used as a famine food in times of scarcity – dried and ground up into a powder and used as a thickening in soups, or mixed with cereals when making bread. The bark itself was used as a source of fibre, from which the Maori people made, particularly, cordage. It was also used to make headbands for porterage, and was woven into baskets, bonnets and the like. The wood of this Hoheria is white and very tough, and was used in cabinet-making. It also burns efficiently to liberate much heat.

The first Ribbonwood tree (*Hoheria populnea*) to arrive in Britain was sent in 1827 by Allan Cunningham (1791–1839). He spent 23 years collecting while based in Eastern Australia, and in 1826 was the first collector to visit New Zealand for the Royal Gardens at Kew. Our species (*H. sexstylosa*), however, was first observed, described and named by William Colenso. He was born in 1811 in Penzance and, although interested in geology and natural history, was indentured and became a printer by trade. He emigrated to New Zealand to run a printing press for the Church Missionary Society, arriving there at the end of December 1834. He met Darwin, when the *Beagle* visited New Zealand in 1835, which enhanced his particular interests in natural history. These interests were further encouraged three years later during a visit by Cunningham, from whom he received some training in plant collecting. He also became the local collector and correspondent for Hooker, after his visits on the *Erebus* in 1841.

Hoheria sexstylosa will grow into a small tree of about 25ft tall, and can be single- or multi-stemmed, with a spread of up to 20 feet. The branching is prolific and dense, and is stiffish and upright, but the branchlets are quite thin and tend to arch and weep, giving the tree a very graceful appearance. On a mature plant the lanceolate, glossy, light-green leaves taper to a point, and are 2–3 inches long and deeply, jaggedly toothed; in juvenile plants the leaves are small and rounded.

The tree looks especially handsome in late July and August, when it is decorated with a mass of fragrant white flowers; after flowering the tree produces curious winged seeds. The flowers are carried in two- to five-flowered cymes in the leaf axils; each has five white petals and is scented; they are about an inch in diameter.

The climate of its native habitats is not dissimilar to the mild and humid, temperate-rainforest climate of Cornwall, so the Hoheria grows and flowers readily here at Heligan. It is hardy along the South Coast, from Sussex westwards. It will grow elsewhere – but will need protection from cold winds and from frost, which may be provided by a wall or an overhead canopy. It is tolerant of a maritime position, and will withstand strong winds, as long as they are not fiercely cold. It grows equally well on both acid and alkaline soils, but would probably prefer the former.

Having been Propagator here at Heligan, my interest is exactly that – how can it be propagated? The easiest method is simply to collect the seeds in Autumn, sow them straight away into trays, and place in a cold frame – or store them dry and sow in Spring. Alternatively, half-ripe cuttings, 2–3ins long, set in a free-draining compost under mist or covered with very thin polythene on a warm bench, work well.

The scented flowers of Hoheria

Magnolia campbellii

Magnolia campbellii *on the Dovecote Lawn*

I experienced both the hurricane of October 1987, in London, and the Great Storm of January 1990, in Cornwall, and recall that surveys in their aftermath suggested Magnolias had proved particularly resilient. One glorious survivor was the only *Magnolia campbellii* among Heligan's veteran tree and shrub collections, for which I have since developed a particular affinity, for the colour of its blooms is like Candy-floss! This spellbinding tree shone out amid the devastation the first time I entered the gardens, only weeks after the blasts had subsided. Driven by a desire to see it again, I discovered it was visible from a considerable distance across the local landscape.

Now the Lost Gardens of Heligan are open to the public, and the early flowering of the *Magnolia campbellii* is perceived to be the herald of our Cornish Spring. Positioned at the back of Flora's Green on the highest ground in the Garden, close to the entrance, its progress through the latter part of Winter is closely and eagerly observed by staff and regular visitors. Its hairy, conical-shaped buds gradually swell on naked branches, and the years when its large pink blooms are prolific are a source of general delight. Against an angry grey or joyous, bright blue sky, or as a carpet of fallen petals, its flowering brings a touch of magic to the Gardens.

A cause for celebration it must also have been for those who first discovered this tree in its native habitat, and for those who acquired its seed and nurtured the first of these trees to flower in England, in the late nineteenth century. (Flowering on trees raised from seed can take up to 30 years, but their life expectancy is more than for most ornamentals; hence at Heligan we could now be enjoying a very early introduction.)

Magnolia campbellii occurs naturally along the Himalayas, from Eastern Nepal, Sikkim and Bhutan to North Assam, at altitudes of 7,000–11,000ft. It is of the subgenus *Yulania* (named after the Oriental *Yulan*, meaning Lily), which includes all the deciduous temperate species from Asia. In the wild it can reach the incredible height of 120ft, while in cultivation in South West England, about half that.

Magnolias occur naturally only in the Northern Hemisphere (America and Asia), and have the most primitive form of flower structure. Their fossil remains can be dated back more than 100 million years. They have the largest individual flowers of any tree or shrub raised outdoors in temperate regions. With no distinction between sepals and petals, the 'floral leaves' named tepals are typically arranged in whorls of three, cupping numerous stamens, attached in spiral formation to a convex receptacle.

Magnolia campbellii has eight outer tepals, which fully open horizontally, like huge (9-inch) saucers, with four inner tepals which remain almost closed until the stigma has begun to wither. Hence direct pollination and fertilisation cannot occur, because the stamens do not shed pollen until the flower is fully open.

Clockwise from top left: Flower bud, new leaves, fruit with seeds, flowers on naked branches

It is only possible if pollination from early-flowering blooms higher up the tree can be achieved by wind or insect gravitation. Each bloom sterile to its own pollen, a mature tree does not customarily produce much fertile fruit. So *M. campbellii* is best propagated by grafting or layering – a procedure first undertaken in England by Veitch's of Exeter in the early 1900s.

It was Dr W. Griffith who, in 1838, first described and pictured the tree that was later named *Magnolia campbellii* (the white version). His drawing, however, was only published posthumously – and just after J.D. Hooker and T. Thomson published the first colour plates in *Illustrations of Himalayan Plants*, in 1855.

In this year Hooker named the Magnolia after Dr Archibald Campbell, his companion on a perilous adventure in 1849 – a small reward for the attack, torture and imprisonment suffered at the hands of Sikkimese soldiers. British Political Agent to Sikkim, based at Darjeeling, Campbell had been involved in negotiating permissions, supplies and protection for Hooker to travel north through Sikkim, plant collecting, and had joined him at the climax of the trip. Their violation of the Sikkim/Tibetan border had prompted their imprisonment, and the Rajah of Sikkim was then warned by the Indian government that unless he released them, his country would be invaded. The naming of this tree is connected with a significant political incident, resulting in India's annexation of part of Sikkim – and the further expansion of Queen Victoria's Empire.

Magnolia delavayi

Magnolia delavayi *flower (above), on the tree presiding over our New Zealand Garden (left)*

Dominating the area known as New Zealand, the *Magnolia delavayi* stands prominently, like a matriarch from a previous generation – tough, aged and somewhat battered. Visitors taking 'time out' on the wishbone seat beneath, are prompted to ask about the overhanging tree. Fortunately, my investigations have enabled me to answer most of their questions.

Digging into the archives and pursuing the literature gave me real enjoyment, and provided an insight into the pioneering spirit of the late nineteenth and early twentieth centuries. It allowed me to conjure up mental pictures of the events leading to the discovery and introduction of *Magnolia delavayi*.

In 1886 the Abbé Delavay, a French missionary, plant enthusiast and collector, first saw and described this plant from the North West of Dali, in Yunnan Province, China. The plant was duly named in his honour, but it was Ernest Henry 'Chinese' Wilson who collected the seed and introduced the species.

Wilson was born in the Cotswolds in 1876. His keen interest in plants, coupled with his botanical knowledge, won him the Queen's Prize for Botany, which enabled him to progress to the Diploma Course at the Royal Botanic Gardens, Kew, where his intelligence and dogged attributes were recognised by W.T. Thistleton-Dyer, Director of Kew, who recommended him to Veitch's Nurseries to travel to China to collect seed of *Davidia involucrata*.

Wilson must have felt considerable trepidation on his embarkation in 1899. He was a young and inexperienced traveller and collector – but he was to travel across the Atlantic from Liverpool to New York, across America by train to San Francisco, and then continue, by boat, to China. The continuation of his journey was arduous and dogged by difficulty. He encountered a grim epidemic of bubonic plague in Hong Kong as he travelled on into Indo-China, to Hanoi (where the French regarded all Englishmen with suspicion). He was held up at the Chinese border by local skirmishes, and braved the constant threat of malaria. Eventually he met up with Augustine Henry in the wilds of Yunnan, to discover the whereabouts of the Davidia, and then, continuing, made his way to Ichang (on the Yangtze), where he established his base on a houseboat. Wilson was just 23 years old, and his venture had already taken him more than 13,000 miles.

The bark, bud (top) and fruit of Magnolia delavayi

In the Autumn of 1899 Wilson collected seeds of *Magnolia delavayi* in Southern Yunnan, where the trees grew on sandstone and limestone formations in Lithocarpus scrub. The Magnolia first flowered at Kew in 1908, under glass.

Here at Heligan early records and surmises suggest that our tree was obtained in 1906/7. It is evident that Jack Tremayne, as an affluent garden-owner and plantsman, was keeping bang up to date with the latest introductions. He was surely purchasing plants from James Veitch & Sons of The Royal Nurseries in Chelsea at that time – as the existence of the Davidia and two Kiwi Fruit plants (all Wilson collections from the same vintage, and the latest commercial introductions) in the Garden would suggest.

Despite its origins at altitudes of only 3,600–7,220 feet in the sub-tropics of Yunnan, *Magnolia delavayi* shows no adverse effects from temperatures as low as -14°C in the British Isles, and demonstrates surprising hardiness. Our specimen has become multi-stemmed with a wide, bushy, evergreen canopy, which is now stag-headed as its top has got above the protection of the surrounding trees, and has regularly been seared by the east wind during the Winter. However, in the way of magnolias it tends to renew itself from the base.

The bark is unusual in that it is corky and ridged, and is a pleasant, fawn-grey colour. The branches, which are generally upright and sometimes intertwined, lead into magnificent large leaves which attach strongly to the stem. They are ovate, large – reaching more than a foot in length – with a dull, dark green upper surface, and a beautiful underneath with an exquisite silvery-grey, soft down. They are among the largest-leaved plants of temperate-climate evergreens. Compared with other magnolias this species flowers later in the season – the large, bullet-shaped buds appear in June/July, and the late summer flowers erupt in August, their ivory-white beauty lasting only two or three days. The flowers are cup-shaped, usually with six to nine tepals, and can achieve a diameter of 8ins. They are best seen at night, as they open and expand during the early evening. The texture is thick and rubbery, and the fragrance is strong – not heady, but a mild, fruity aroma, somewhat reminiscent of a melon. The flowers remind me of the bracts of *Cornus capitata*. After flowering, a cone-like fruit remains, which is about 6ins long, and hard – very similar to the bud, except for its rigid, layered appearance.

Magnolia grandiflora 'Exmouth'

New trees in the Flower Garden, with the original specimen left of centre, behind the wall

This Magnolia – the Bull Bay (*M. grandiflora*) of Florida and South Carolina – grows into a tall, substantial evergreen tree, with a summer-flowering habit and sweetly scented flowers. It was planted extensively in the front of early homesteads in the Southern United States, and widely celebrated in literature and song, for the shade it provides and the scent of its flowers. Dr John Sims, writing in *Curtis' Botanical Magazine* in 1817, describes this tree thus:

> 'The long, laurel leaved Magnolia of South Carolina and Florida must be esteemed as one of the finest trees of the world, growing with a straight trunk, two feet in diameter to upwards of seventy feet high, and forming a regular head. It bears a profusion of flowers which perfume the air around it with a most agreeable scent. In the autumn the fruit, a kind of cone containing scarlet seeds which drop from their cells, and remain suspended by a thread, is scarcely less attractive.'

The date of the introduction of this Magnolia to Europe is uncertain. Although it had been brought to France by 1710, it was probably not cultivated in England until the mid- to late 1720s. The plant at Heligan, in the Sundial Garden, is almost certainly a nineteenth-century planting – dating from the creation of that garden for Mrs John (Lady) Tremayne. It is, almost certainly, the variety described as the Exmouth Magnolia, as this was the only plant being propagated locally at that time, and seed propagation had not yet succeeded.

Philip Miller, in his *Figures of Plants* (1760), illustrates *Magnolia grandiflora*, and writes: 'The largest tree of its kind which I have met with in England is in the garden of Sir John Colliton at Exmouth in Devonshire, which has produced flowers for several years.' The origin of the commercial distribution of this plant is described by J.C. Loudon in the *Gardener's Magazine* (1835). He cites a Thomas Tupman, who stated that his father (who had been gardener to Sir Francis Drake) rented the garden after the death of Sir John Colliton, from a Mr Zorn, who had become the proprietor. He then proceeded to intensively propagate the plant by layering the branches into tubs of soil – these were supported on scaffolding which completely surrounded the tree – and selling the progeny at half a guinea a plant. Virtually all the veteran plants in Devon and Cornwall are descended from this tree. The garden then passed into the hands of a Mr Davis of Exeter, when, in the mid-1790s, the tree unfortunately came to an untimely end. A labourer sent to fell an old apple tree levelled the Magnolia to the ground instead! By that time the trunk was 1ft 6ins in diameter.

Clockwise from top: Single flower on a new tree; single fruit on the old. The original still blooms for much of the year

The leaves are lanceolate, often slightly curled under at the margins, long (up to 10ins) and relatively narrow; shiny, soft green on the upper surface, and lightly felted with a red-brown indumentum underneath – the older leaves gradually losing the felt. The leaves last for nearly two years.

The flowers are large – up to 10ins across – and normally consist of between 12 and 18 tepals. The tepals are individually thick, waxy and pure white, surrounding the prominent central boss of carpels and stamens. They are goblet-shaped as they open, but gradually flatten out. The blooms are produced in a flush just after mid-Summer, but sporadic flower production occurs throughout the rest of the Summer and into the Autumn. The flowers are sweetly scented and last about three days – the stamens are shed on the second day, leaving a deep red collar below the carpels.

In the early days the plant was perceived as marginally hardy, so was generally given a south or west wall of the House, where the improved temperature also helped to set flower buds. However, the need to train it against the wall and constrain it from taking up too much forward space generally meant that flower production was subdued by pruning; hence the encouragement of vegetative growth. Nowadays it grows perfectly well, especially in the South and West, as a freestanding large shrub or tree, provided that it is reasonably sheltered.

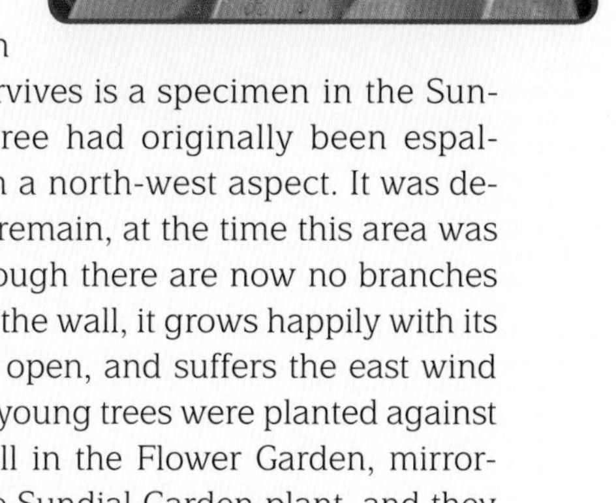

The only tree in the Gardens that survives is a specimen in the Sundial Garden. This tree had originally been espaliered on a wall with a north-west aspect. It was decided that it should remain, at the time this area was recovered, and although there are now no branches left below the top of the wall, it grows happily with its head well up in the open, and suffers the east wind lightly. In 1996 four young trees were planted against the north-facing wall in the Flower Garden, mirroring the aspect of the Sundial Garden plant, and they have since been espaliered with the object of supplying cut flowers. By 2006 these trees were just coming into production.

Podocarpus totara

The Podocarpus totara *by Second Pond in the Jungle*

The Totara, *Podocarpus totara*, is a marginally hardy tree of the Yew family from New Zealand, a large and healthy specimen of which stands by Second Pond – about a third of the way down the eastern side of the Jungle, dominating the area. It was probably planted by Jack Tremayne, while working with his father, Squire John Tremayne. They transformed this area from an apple orchard into a showcase for semi-hardy plants – the basis of the Jungle. This sheltered valley has a unique microclimate, and maintains a temperature up to five degrees warmer than the Northern Gardens, providing a home for sub-tropical and other tender plants. The Tremaynes' foresight in choosing this less than hardy tree (at least when young) has been vindicated, and we benefit from an unusually fine and handsome mature specimen.

This particular Totara tree has a noteworthy claim to fame as, according to Alan Mitchell (the surveyor for the Tree Register of Britain and Ireland), it is the largest specimen of the species in the UK, and possibly in Europe. Its current height is estimated at about 75 feet, but because of its position on a steep gradient it does not grow erectly, but leans and has developed into a large and spreading tree.

In the eighth edition of Bean's *Trees and Shrubs Hardy in the British Isles* (1988), the largest *Podocarpus totara* trees in the UK were recorded as being at Trebah, Tregrehan, Menabilly and Bosahan (all in Cornwall). However, these records were published in 1984, prior to the rediscovery of Heligan's plant heritage. It is probable that this tree was planted in the mid-1890s – as virtually all except bone-hardy plants would have been killed off by the Great Freeze of April 1891, particularly if they were young and newly planted. This speculative planting date would suggest that the tree is over 100 years old. However, this is a comparatively youthful age for a Totara – the largest trees in its native New Zealand have been estimated at 500 years old (but may be up to 1,800 years old), and easily exceed 150 feet in height.

With its roots spreading into the free-draining soil adjacent to the Pond, there is plenty of moisture available – beloved of many trees and shrubs native to New Zealand. This, combined with the mild, Atlantic climate of Cornwall, has encouraged the tree to thrive.

The name Podocarpus is derived from the Greek *pous* (a foot) and *karpos* (a fruit), referring to the shape of the fruit stalks. The species is dioecious, so male and female flowers are borne on separate plants. Heligan's plant is male, and releases vast amounts of wind-disseminated pollen, which rises in a huge, cloud-like plume – a display triggered by the breeze during the early hours of a late spring morning. This memorable sight can last for several minutes. Early visitors and gardeners pause transfixed as they watch this unusual phenomenon – but the show is to no avail as there is no female tree here with its receptive cones to allow successful pollination. A sapling tree has recently been planted in the vicinity, but it will probably be 50 years before it flowers, and even then who knows whether it will be female?

The leaves are evergreen and are scattered, or are in two ranks along the stems – each being about ¾in in length and ¼in in width on a mature specimen such as ours. The trunk of the tree is distinctive, as the bark sheds lengthways, gradually peeling off and dangling in characteristic long slabs hanging from the trunk.

This large Podocarp is nowadays a significant, integral part of the Jungle scene. Its sweeping branches dip low over Second Pond, creating a dense canopy. If you stand back at a distance and gaze up to the crown of the tree in Spring, it is likely that you will see the delicate white blossoms of *Clematis armandii*, supported high up on the strong, lofty boughs.

Clockwise from top: A cockerel in the Totara; buds on the old tree; Totara draped in Clematis armandii*; foliage*

The bark creates an ideal substrate for a miniature, epiphytic orchid, *Dendrobium kingianum*, which is secured in mossy hollows. All the nutrients required by the plant are obtained from the rivulets of water running down the trunk, and from the dripping of the overhanging branches.

In its native country the Totara is an important timber tree. The wood, which is straight grained and reddish in colour, is very durable in water, and it was therefore important and valuable to the indigenous Maori population in the construction of their massive war canoes. Other traditional uses involved drinking an infusion of the leaves to treat fevers, and the use of the strong wood as splints.

In our climate the Totara is so slow growing that it is often recommended for topiary and hedge work, but given correct siting with a suitable climatic niche, it can develop as a fine tree.

Pseudotsuga menziesii

The old Douglas Fir at the top of the Ravine can be seen from the far end of Flora's Green

Pseudotsuga menziesii, the magnificent Douglas Fir, is a coniferous, forest tree from the Pacific slopes of Western North America, where it is the predominant forest tree from British Columbia southwards to mid-California. It can grow to as much as 300ft tall, with a bole which can be 8–12ft in diameter. Yet in the natural habitat the trees grow very close together, often only a few feet apart. But, given space, it will grow into a pyramidal-shaped tree, with a short, cylindrical crown which becomes flat at maturity. On older trees, the lower trunk tends to be bare of branches, as demonstrated by the specimens at Heligan.

To grow at its best this fir needs a combination of a moderately good, moisture-retentive soil, abundant rainfall (40–60ins a year), and relatively consistent humidity.

The branches are densely clothed in deep green, relatively short (about one inch long) leaves which have a slightly rounded tip. The foliage emits a strong, fruity smell when bruised. The leaves are carried in two rows on either side of the branchlets (as in the genus *Abies*), but with a V-shaped arrangement. The bark on young trees is smooth and greyish, but as it ages it becomes thickened, red-brown in colour, with ridges and deep furrows and a cork-like texture. The cones are 3–4ins long and 1½–2ins wide. They consist of numerous thin, light, rounded, brown scales, which mature in August and shed the seeds during the Autumn.

The wood is highly prized, and employed for the same purposes as larch and pitch-pine. Because of its potentially great size and useful wood, this species has become one of the most important lumber trees in the world.

The tree was first noted and described by Archibald Menzies *c.*1793 when accompanying Vancouver on his circumnavigation, but he was unable to collect specimens for introduction. Menzies' bad luck was the good fortune of his fellow Scot, David Douglas, who collected seed and sent it back in 1827. It is with these two men that the name of this fir will always be associated.

Douglas was born in 1799 in the village of Scone, the son of a mason. At the age of eleven he began a seven-year apprenticeship as a gardener on the estate of the 3rd Earl of Mansfield at Scone Palace.

He was fond of books and educated himself in botany, acquiring a good knowledge of native and exotic plants. Having completed and excelled in his apprenticeship, he spent two years in the gardens of Sir Robert Preston at Valleyfield in Fife. Here he had access to the proprietor's extensive botanical and zoological library, and worked with his choice collection of exotic plants. His endeavours brought him to the notice of Dr W.J. Hooker, Professor of Botany at the University of Glasgow (later the first Director of Kew), and he secured a position to accompany him on botanical expeditions in Scotland. It was Hooker who suggested to the Horticultural Society of London that Douglas would make a most suitable plant collector for the Society.

In 1823 Douglas made his first trip – to the East Coast of North America, where he collected particularly fruit trees, but also many other new plants for cultivation in Great Britain. When he returned from this trip he was dispatched on an extended collecting trip to the West Coast of North America, to expand especially on Menzies' observations of giant conifers. Through the good offices of the Hudson Bay Company, he landed at Fort Vancouver on the Columbia River in 1825. From then until his return in 1827 he sent back an important array of beautiful and interesting plants, both as seeds and dried specimens – among them, what was to become known as the Douglas Fir. In 1829 he returned to the Columbia River, collecting down into California, making a trip to the Sandwich Islands (Hawaii), returning to Columbia and making a trip to the Fraser River.

Clockwise from top: The necklace of Witch's Broom; foliage and new cones on a mature tree; the bark. The young tree at the top of the Ravine (below)

His success as a collector was due not only to his plant knowledge, but also to his ability to survive the hazards encountered and to create a rapport with the native Americans whom he recruited as guides. In 1833 he left North America for the Sandwich Islands, having resigned as the Society's collector. It was here that he met his death when he fell into an already occupied wild-cattle pit trap and was gored to death.

There are a few surviving Douglas Firs at Heligan. One is at the top end of the Ravine. It was probably planted *c.*1870–80. In the windy Cornish climate it is not faring well now, but its interest is enhanced by the tight necklace of Witch's Broom encircling the tree at about 20 feet. Another overlooks the eastern side of the Jungle.

A replacement tree has been planted at the corner of Flora's Green, in memory of Douglas Holland, an early Friend of Heligan. An unstinting supporter, it was he who first pointed out that 'Heligan' is an anagram of 'Healing'.

Pyrus 'Swan's Egg'

Pyrus *'Swan's Egg' (above); a blackbird enjoys fallen fruit (left)*

Trained fruit trees were a must in any Victorian kitchen garden, with many benefiting from a sheltered wall to protect flower buds and to hasten ripening. These trees not only demonstrated the skill of the gardeners but allowed intensive cropping and the production of high-quality fruit.

Today one such original tree remains on the north-facing wall of the Melon Yard. It is a Swan's Egg pear that was once espaliered, but years of neglect and ensuing undergrowth have resulted in a fully grown tree with an 'L'-shaped kink in its trunk. Nevertheless, it still obliges every year by cropping copiously.

Swan's Egg is a late-ripening small perry pear being first described by Mr Batty Langley in 1729. It has rough, greenish skin almost covered with brown russetting; its flesh is white, firm and not particularly gritty. On maturity the fruit is juicy with a musky flavour and not unpleasant to eat.

The blossom and fruit of Pyrus *'Swan's Egg' (above). The tree grows near the old Tool Shed in the Melon Yard. The kink in the trunk shows clearly (right)*

Perry pears are hybrids of *Pyrus communis* and *Pyrus nivalis*, which are both native to Central Europe. Generally, under orchard conditions, they become much larger, long-lived trees (sometimes living up to 300 years!) and thrive on heavy clay soil, which does not suit cider apple production.

Perry is made like cider – by crushing and pressing the fruit and then setting the juice to ferment. The juice contains varying amounts of natural sorbitol, which adds extra sweetness to the final drink but also acts as a laxative! Perry has been made in Britain since Roman times, though the seventeenth and eighteenth centuries seem to have been when production, particularly in the counties of Gloucestershire, Herefordshire and Worcestershire, reached its peak. There are scores of perry pear varieties – mostly limited to local use and surviving only in neglected orchards, against the odds, because of their robustness and longevity.

Rhododendron arboreum

Rhododendron arboreum

The name most commonly associated with the introduction of the Indian *Rhododendron arboreum* into England is that of Joseph Dalton Hooker. There were several very small-scale imports in the early years of the nineteenth century but it was Hooker who first sent large quantities of seed to this country from the slopes of the Himalayas.

Hooker first came across *Rhododendron arboreum* in Darjeeling, while staying with his friend 'Dear old Brian' Hodgson, waiting for his permissions to begin his expedition into Sikkim. There he found it growing abundantly between 5,000 and 10,000 feet, often covering whole hillsides; it must have been a magnificent sight. The collection and transport of the seed was not without difficulties and in a letter written to his father in 1849, he complains:

> 'Alas, one of my finest collections of Rhododendrons sent to Darjeeling got ruined by the coolies falling ill and being detained on the road, so I have to collect the troublesome things afresh. If your shins were as bruised as mine tearing through the interminable Rhododendron scrub, you would be as sick of the sight of these glories as I am.'

Rhododendron arboreum has the appearance of a small tree with a single trunk and can grow to 60ft tall. The leaves, dark green and shapely, have a protective covering on the underside, the indumentum. This is sometimes white, especially at lower elevations, and more often gingery-brown at higher levels. As the altitude from which the plants originate increases, so the indumentum becomes thicker, the leaves decrease in size, and become darker in colour.

The flowers are bell-shaped and borne in nearly globular trusses, often containing 20 or more florets. The colour varies: those with white flowers are found at the higher altitudes; the pink and scarlet ones at the middle altitudes and the deep, glowing red ones on the lower slopes.

It was the dark red variety that was so particularly prized when these plants first flowered in England. There are still a few of these specimens at Heligan, although some are now in poor condition. They have proved to be less hardy than the paler colours, originating as they do from lower elevations. Early nurserymen often used these plants because of their flower colour, to cross with other, hardier species to produce hybrids with greater resistance to frost.

Clockwise from top left: Leaves of Rhododendron arboreum ssp cinnamomeum, *flowers of* R. arboreum, R. arboreum *hybrids on Flora's Green. Below:* R. arboreum *can grow to 60ft tall*

John Tremayne, Squire at Heligan when the first rhododendrons arrived here during the 1850s, was an enthusiastic hybridiser, and Heligan has a number of these bright red hybrids that are believed to have been raised by him, notably the group that stretches along the south side of Flora's Green. There is also a particularly good tree growing in the Jungle.

Only one of these deep red rhododendrons has ever been given an individual name. It is called, appropriately, *Rhododendron* 'Heligan', and grows just beside the front door of Heligan House.

The red *Rhododendron arboreum* is the dominant parent of the hybrids known as 'Cornish Red', of which there are several large groups around the northern side of Flora's Green and in the Jungle.

One of the variations of *Rhododendron arboreum* is the sub-species *cinnamomeum*, which has pretty pink or white flowers with rust-coloured indumentum on the underside of the leaves. It was originally called *R. campbelliae* and was named for the wife of Dr Archibald Campbell, with whom Joseph Hooker shared some of his adventures in Sikkim. Hooker wrote to his father on 18th July, 1848:

> 'I wrote and told him (Campbell) this morning that I would ask you to confirm the name of a Rhododendron on his wife, a little compliment that has touched him to the quick; he is very much attached to his wife, and I really never saw a man so heartily appreciate a trifling favour.'

There are several *Rhododendron arboreum ssp cinnamomeum* at Heligan: a pale pink variety behind the Chusan Palms close to the entrance to the Flower Garden, and a pretty white-flowered one on the eastern side of the Jungle.

Rhododendron falconeri

Rhododendron falconeri
beside the Head Gardener's Office

Entry Rhododendrons, stamens 10–20
1 R Falconeri
2 R Campanulatum
3 R Griffithianum
4 R Argenteum
5 R Auklandii

This is an extract from the Goods Inward Journal at Kew, and is part of a list that records and describes a consignment of seeds that had arrived at Kew from India, sent by Joseph Dalton Hooker.

Hooker was just thirty when he set off for India in 1847. With no personal fortune, he had a small stipend of £450 per year from the Admiralty; little enough to cover the expenses of his expeditions, let alone pay for the many instances of help and hospitality he received. He was later ble to reward those whose encouragement and friendship contributed greatly to the success of his travels: he named plants for them.

One such friend was Dr Hugh Falconer, an employee of the HEIC, and Superintendant of the Bombay Botanical Gardens. He provided hospitality, local botanical advice and encouragement, and he was particularly helpful to Hooker in that he acted as agent for the dispatch of the collections from Calcutta to England. It is a happy chance that one of the most impressive trees to come from this expedition should have been named after a man with such a fine name.

Hooker first saw *Rhododendron falconeri* near Darjeeling in 1848 as he was trekking through the valley of the Great Rungreet River. If you stand beneath the enormous and venerable specimen of this rhododendron outside the Flower Garden, you can imagine his wonder on seeing it for the first time.

This species is beautiful on many counts. First you see its smooth, sinuous limbs, deep mahogany dappled with darker patches and, where the bark is sheltered, the outer layers peel off in milk chocolate curls. As you follow the bare branches, snaking up into the foliage, you see the underside of the leaves, a deep, rich, gingery colour, velvety to the touch, that contrasts with the dark green, matt upper surface. The true glory comes in May when, in a good year, this magnificent old rhododendron is covered with several hundred huge flower heads, great candelabra of creamy-yellow flowers, each one the size of a melon. Standing beneath, you can peer up into the waxy bells to see the deep purple flashes inside. This tree is now more than 30ft high, and with a greater spread. It is among the oldest in England, and has been here at Heligan for 150 years, raised from a seed no bigger than a speck of dust, sent from India.

This particular plant has had a chequered existence over the last 50 years or so. The ground around it gradually eroded away as adjacent paths consolidated, so that eventually it was growing on a small hillock well above the surrounding level. As a consequence, the water was flowing off during the Summer, and the tree was becoming far too dry. Its continued existence became doubtful. The situation was remedied in 2001 when a retaining drystone wall was built around it, and the area around the roots filled with a suitable soil mix, in the hope that this would extend the life and happiness of this venerable specimen. So far so good!

Rhododendron falconeri: *The velvety underside of the leaves (above), and sinuous limbs among primulas, with Bothy behind (below)*

The seeds of this rhododendron were often collected in physically dangerous circumstances, and in politically difficult situations. They were collected by teams of porters, local Indians whom Hooker had trained for the purpose. The seeds were then cleaned, packed into cotton bags and then into cases for their long, often hazardous journey from the wilds of Sikkim to England. At Kew, the arrival of this cargo was meticulously recorded, before being sent to Kew's own nurseries for propagation, to commercial nurseries anxious to raise these exciting new species, and as gifts to friends and sponsors.

There are other fine specimens of this species at Heligan. One is at the east end of Flora's Green, where it is the last of the tree rhododendrons to flower, making a spectacular end to the season. There is another near the Reservoir, another on the edge of Sikkim, and yet others in the Jungle. Young specimens have also been planted recently in several places in the Northern Gardens.

Rhododendron niveum

The flower of Rhododendron niveum

Rhododendron hymenanthus ssp niveum. Roughly translated, this means 'a plant the size and shape of a tree, whose flowers are like roses and with leaves that look like snow'. This is the simplified version; its full name goes on to suggest that, although very similar to *R. arboreum*, it is subtly different and therefore classified into a sub-genus.

Its name is burden enough, but not the only grief this plant has to bear. It has a history.

Heligan has a fine specimen of *Rhododendron niveum*. It was planted, probably in the late 1850s, on the northern edge of Flora's Green, where its free-flowering habit makes it an impressive sight. It is one of the famous Sikkim rhododendrons introduced from India by Sir Joseph Dalton Hooker.

The leathery leaves are dark green, the undersides covered with a pale down – not snow-white as its name suggests, more of a pleasing soft, silvery colour. Flowers appear in late March or early April. The round trusses are tight packed with firm, fleshy florets, cool and satisfying to cup in your hand. But the colour! The colour is its downfall, the reason for its misfortune. It is mauve; described by some as 'ashy' or 'dirty'. Although admittedly some specimens do not have the clear colour of the Heligan plant, these seem harsh words indeed.

For a while, during the later part of the nineteenth century, *Rhododendron niveum* enjoyed great popularity, and was widely planted in Victorian gardens, but the plants then appeared to lose favour. Many were uprooted and consigned to the bonfire.

So, why this sudden demise, this relegation to the flames? Blame James Hargreaves and his Spinning Jenny, invented in 1764. Machines such as these enabled the abundant supply of cheap raw material from India and the Americas to be manufactured into relatively inexpensive cotton cloth. By the middle of the nineteenth century, the production of cotton had overtaken that of wool.

Cheap material required cheap dyes; not for the working classes the product of Mediterranean molluscs. The Victorian version of Tyrian purple that was to prove so successful was the accidental result of a chemical experiment performed by the young William Perkin in 1856. The resulting aniline dye produced a purple colour called mauveine. This colour became very fashionable for a number of years – so much so that Queen Victoria wore a silk gown dyed mauveine to the opening of the International Exhibition in 1862. By the 1870s, however, as the dye became more readily available, it was used in the cheap cotton from which the uniforms of domestic staff and hospital nurses were made – an association that quickly made the colour unacceptable to the fashionable world.

Hence the problem. The Victorian pleasure gardens were there to give enjoyment to their leisured and affluent owners, who had no wish to be reminded of their lowly employees, and the pale purple of the niveum now offended the eye – so out came the niveums!

Rhododendron niveum *bud and leaves (above); in full bloom (right); in colourful context (below)*

There is an alternative explanation for their demise. When rhododendrons were first planted, they were often used in borders as part of a planned colour scheme and, although on a mature tree, the mauve of the flowers make an attractive contrast with the white felted leaves, it is easy to understand why such a colour would not have fitted easily into a mixed planting, and undoubtedly the flowers of some specimens are very drab. Perhaps it was aesthetics, therefore, rather than social snobbery that resulted in the removal of so many of these rhododendrons.

Why was the one at Heligan spared? Was John Tremayne more egalitarian than many of his counterparts, or less concerned with considerations of colour or fashion? Certainly he was a plantsman, an enthusiastic collector of new and exotic plants that were pouring into England from all parts of the expanding Victorian world. It would, no doubt, have been a source of great satisfaction to him to possess a plant from the first introduction of this particular species; a satisfaction more important than class sensibilities. Whatever the explanation, the *Rhododendron niveum* at Heligan is a rarity.

Sequoiadendron giganteum

Sequoiadendron giganteum *in the Jungle (above), and looking up the fibrous trunk (right)*

The Wellingtonia (*Sequoiadendron giganteum*) of California is one of a number of coniferous trees known as Redwoods. They are classified as members of the Cupressaceae family (which includes the Cypresses and Cryptomerias). Its nearest relatives are the Coast Redwood (*Sequoia sempervirens*) and the Dawn Redwood (*Metasequoia glyptostroboides*).

They are known to be the largest life form on earth and can live for up to 3,500 years and grow to over 300ft tall. Their considerable bole size, up to 90ft in girth, represents a massive volume for a single living plant. At Heligan they are known as the grandfathers of the Jungle. Their sheer weight and size helps to protect plants growing close by and creates a unique jungle microclimate.

The trees are native to the western slopes of the Sierra Nevada Mountains in California; they sporadically occupy a territory around 260 miles long and 15 miles wide, at elevations between 4,300ft and 8,000ft. They occur in groves of varying numbers separated by other coniferous species.

The Cornishman William Lobb who had been in California collecting plants for the Veitch Nurseries brought seeds and cones of this exciting new conifer back to the UK in December 1853. He had heard about the trees at a meeting of the California Academy of Sciences, and immediately set off to locate them and collect material. It was his third plant-hunting trip for the firm, which he cut short on finding the tree so that he could be the first to introduce it to Europe. Little did he know that he wouldn't be the first. Only four months earlier a Scot, John Mathew (a private collector), had taken some seed back to Scotland where he distributed it to friends and family. However, Lobb had brought back large quantities of seed, and Veitch made a considerable commercial success from the venture. As a result this tree is now a common sight in Britain especially through lowland Devon, the Veitch Nursery being situated in Exeter.

The tree was immediately described and named *Wellingtonia gigantea*, by Dr Linley, in honour of the recently deceased Duke of Wellington. This created huge dismay in the USA, where it was assumed that they should have the right to name such an important native treasure. There followed a vigorous cross-Atlantic campaign to name the tree after their national hero – Washington. This argument raged on until 1939 when J. Bucholz pointed out a number of unique botanical combinations and he created Sequoiadendron as a genus for it. *Sequoiadendron giganteum* nowadays is the generally accepted name.

The Wellingtonias at Heligan probably date from the 1870s, when the first plantings were made in the area that eventually became the Jungle. Typical growth rate for a healthy tree in Cornwall can be 2ft a year, which will start to slow as the tree matures. The Cornish climate offers favourable conditions for the Redwood which, although is hardy down to -10°C, dislikes extremely high or low temperatures. The Cornish mist has its uses too; the tree slowly captures water suspended in mist, this drips down its needles, limbs and trunk and can help sustain the tree in drier periods. Roots of mature trees usually extend 100ft or more but few roots extend deeper than 3ft, and some even shallower in areas with a high water table. This is remarkable for the size of the tree and it's surprising that many Sequoias remain standing for so long.

The Wellingtonia (like most conifers) is monoecious; the male and female cones are separate and form on the same tree in late Summer. Pollination takes place in the following late Spring with fertilisation delayed into the Summer. A mature Redwood produces some 1,500 new cones annually with a further 10,000 to 30,000 cones still on the tree in various stages of maturity. Like all coniferous trees Sequoias are wind pollinated but they also depend on other factors to help distribute their seeds. Squirrels eat the fleshy scales of the cones and, owing to low nutritional value, disregard the seeds. Beetles mine the cones, causing them to shrink and dry, and allowing the seed to fall. Fire in the forest dries the cones, releasing enormous amounts of seed.

The bark is very characterful, reddish brown in colour, very fibrous and furrowed and can be up to 2ft thick. Tannin is a substance that gives the bark its reddish colour; it is also abundant in the cones and at one time was used to treat burns on humans. If the tree is wounded tannin covers the wound, protecting the tree from decay and possibly insects and diseases.

Redwoods are friendly trees not restricting other species; nowadays they are prized for their ornamental value by gardeners and there has been recent interest in the States for utilising them in Christmas tree plantations. They provide excellent wind shelter and a diverse habitat for wildlife, but they do require plenty of room both above and below ground. Patience is another requirement, as these trees are in no rush to mature and will outgrow the many generations of gardeners that plant them.

Sequoiadendron giganteum • Michelle Griffiths

Sorbus devoniensis

Julian Stephens and Peter Stafford hunt for the old Otmast tree

At a Friends' Evening in 2002, we were handed a copy of some documents relating to Heligan that had come to light in the Courtney Library of Truro Museum. One concerned the collection and use of a fruit called 'Otmast', which allegedly grew (in 1912) on a tree(s) here at Heligan. These fruits were said to have been much prized by Squire Jack Tremayne for 'stuffing cooked pheasants'. The writer goes on to suggest that the fruits were more highly prized than the birds! The location of the trees was described as being 'down the horse lane from Peruppa to Heligan House', and 'in the wood below Nancellan Lane End at Temple'. Much time and effort did not turn up any useful information for the identification of this tree – it was speculated that they were the fruit of, among others, *Cornus capitata* or an Osmanthus. However, as a result of a query in the Friends Newsletter, a solution began to take shape.

Mrs Ford, from Mevagissey, who is a long-time Friend of Heligan, came to see us and told us the following:

Mrs Ford's father, a renowned Mevagissey fisherman named Preston Thomas, was widely travelled, and knew Jack Tremayne. It was he who had introduced his daughter and her life-long friend Pat to the Otmast fruit (both ladies were quite specific about the name as they had discussed it frequently over the years). The two ladies (who were young girls at the time) accompanied Preston Thomas each Autumn in the late 1930s and early 1940s 'to a tree, near a walnut tree, somewhere around Peruppa'. Mr Thomas also took Mr Ford to another tree 'beyond Temple Wood near Nancellan Lane'. They were only ever shown these two trees.

Mr Thomas would get up into the trees and throw down the fruits, which would be eaten on the spot. They were mature trees in the 1930s – so now would be at least 100 years old. The fruit was delicious to eat raw, and had a 'rich' taste. Mr Ford remembered that the taste was not dissimilar to that of a Medlar – but with a different consistency.

So where to go from here? Mr Ford offered to try to find one of these trees, and set off on many an expedition, but without success. The one by Peruppa has not yet been found, but, would you believe it – after many fruitless (no pun intended) trips he did indeed find the tree down by Nancellan Lane.

Not only that, but, fortunately, it was Autumn, and there were fruits lying on the ground. These matched their recollections precisely. The tree was old, decrepit and overgrown, so the fruits were not up to much; but we did now have twigs, fruits and a few last leaves.

So what was this mysterious tree? It was definitely a *Sorbus* of the Whitebeam/ Service Tree type, but we needed to be more specific. Thus our sample was sent to Westonbirt Arboretum, and the reply confirmed it as *Sorbus devoniensis* or 'French Hales'. W.J. Bean (*Trees and Shrubs Hardy in the British Isles*) says '*S. devoniensis* is commonest in North Devon and its fruits were once sold in Barnstaple market. It also occurs in South Devon and East Cornwall. It is a genuine species which breeds true from seed'.

This Sorbus is one of many very localised species, which are variations that have become stabilised as a result of the production of apomictic seed – seed which is vegetatively produced, without any fertilisation. The trees, when grown from seed, are therefore virtually all the same.

A new Otmast, which we have planted in the Poultry Orchard

The outstanding mystery then related to the name 'Otmast'. It was certainly a very local name, and was probably a pet name of Jack Tremayne, which was picked up by Preston Thomas. 'Mast' is an old English word for the fruit of a forest tree – as in Beech mast. 'Ot' has two possible derivations – both, however, as suffixes. The first meaning is 'belonging to' as in 'zealot' or 'Cypriot'. The second meaning is something 'small', as in ballot – a small ball. Mastot would not slip off the tongue easily, so why not 'Otmast'? This is our best guess.

The tree, when free standing, grows to 20 feet tall, with a roundish head and the typical leaves of a Whitebeam or Service tree – which are more or less oval and dark green, with a distinct white felt on the underside. The umbels of white flowers are produced in Spring, followed by the sprigs of globular, orange-red berries – about a third of an inch in diameter. These are hard and coarse textured, but, when fully ripe, are soft and sweet; in effect they 'blet' in the same way as the fruit of Medlars (*Mespilus germanica*) or the Chequer Tree (*Sorbus torminalis*).

Stauntonia hexaphylla

Bright green Stauntonia hexaphylla *on the wall in the Sundial Garden*

Stauntonia hexaphylla, an unusual climbing plant from the Far East, is a member of the family *Lardizabalaceae*, which also includes Akebia and Holboellia, and is still reasonably uncommon in cultivation. At Heligan it can be found on the wall in the Sundial Garden (aka Mrs Tremayne's Flower Garden), towards the bottom end, by the southern gate into the Flower Garden.

In 1995, when we came to clear this totally overgrown area in order to recreate the Sundial Garden (filmed for the first Channel 4 TV documentary), a few plants were reprieved – this one among them. The clearance was intended to be rigorous and complete, in order to provide an uninterrupted palette for the development and creation of the new garden. The greater proportion of plants found in this area were indeed weeds (herbaceous and woody) which had grown up and choked the space. However, a few plants had survived, and it was deemed that some of these deserved a second chance, partly because of their rarity or interest, but also because of their tenacity. The Davidia and the *Magnolia grandiflora* were obvious candidates, but it was not until we were clearing some willow scrub and *Rhododendron ponticum* near the bottom against the wall that this plant was found – it had been growing and surviving amid all the competition for more than three generations, and we didn't have the heart to destroy it!

It evidently has an early provenance at Heligan, as Thurston (*British and Foreign Trees and Shrubs in Cornwall*, 1930) notes this species 'growing on a wall at Heligan'. It must have been sufficiently substantial to be noticed soon after the Great War.

The Stauntonia is generally described as a modest climber, usually growing to 6–8ft, but this probably represents a young plant – our specimen is particularly vigorous, and needs to be cut down every five years or so in order to constrain it to a reasonable area of wall (12ft wide by 14ft tall). This vigour no doubt reflects the fact that its rootstock is probably more than 100 years old, and consequently well established. The plant is a twining, scrambling, vigorous climber with strong, slender stems; the compound leaves usually have five leaflets (but varying from three to seven – the specific name *hexaphylla* suggests six leaflets – emanating, on stalks, from the end of the main leaf stalk in an arc). Each leaflet is about 2ins in length. This makes a dense, intertwining mass of stems and leaves through trees or shrubs, but it needs support on a wall. In our mild climate it is evergreen. The leaves are glossy, leathery and a mid-green, which darkens as the Summer progresses.

There is considerable discrepancy in the literature as to how the flowers are arranged, and the shape of the fruits. The flowers are certainly unisexual, but are said to be dioecious – by some

Clockwise from top left: Leaves, fruit, trunk and flowers of Stauntonia hexaphylla

authorities; others describe them as monoecious. In the *Lardizabalaceae* the male flowers often occur at the tip, and female flowers below in the same raceme. However, Roy Lancaster (in *The Hillier Manual of Trees and Shrubs*) says that they occur in separate racemes. Our plant has the first type of arrangement. Flowering occurs in the Spring. Individual flowers are ¾ inch across, with six whitish sepals (no petals), with a violet tinge. There are from three to seven flowers in a raceme, and they are scented.

The fruits on our plant are about the size and shape of a Victoria plum, and are soft and pulpy, with a softly flushed, purple-pink skin. They are edible, but insipid in the same way that the Kiwi Fruit's flavour may be described. The shiny black seeds are also a hindrance.

The plant was introduced to the United Kingdom in 1874, and was named in honour of Sir George Staunton – a medical doctor who had accompanied Lord Macartney on his famous 1793 embassy to China. It was noted growing at Kew in 1876.

In modern literature the natural distribution of this species is described as 'from Korea, Japan and the Ryukyu Islands to Taiwan'. Descriptions of the plant vary, especially in relation to the size, shape and colour of the fruit. Roy Cheek (*Journal of the Royal Horticultural Society*, 1990) supposes that this extensive distribution (which involves so many islands, and hence the potential for variation) would probably mean that it has been introduced from a number of divergent sources. The plants available at the time our specimen was planted (possibly the 1880s) were clonal, having been propagated from cuttings, probably from a single original introduced plant.

Trachycarpus fortunei

Trachycarpus fortunei *in the Northern Gardens. An unusual winter view (above); the same planting seen from the Vegetable Garden in Spring (left)*

Trachycarpus fortunei – the Chusan Palm or Chinese Windmill Palm – is probably the hardiest of the tall, upright-growing tree palms, and is one of the very few palms which can be successfully grown, with confidence, in most parts of Southern England. It can also be grown in mild niches further north. But it is particularly successful in the favoured climatic niches of Cornwall, and there are specimens in various gardens (especially at Trebah) which are in excess of 45ft tall. These are among the tallest in the country.

The Chusan Palm has been, and is, widely cultivated in South East Asia, China and Japan, where the fibres of the old leaf stalks, which clothe the stem, are extracted and used variously for making brushes and rope, and as a constituent of coarse cloths. It is also used extensively in Mediterranean and other warm temperate climates as a reliable ornamental, when a fan palm of tree stature is designated for a particular setting. The native distribution of this palm is much debated. It is nowadays difficult to determine its natural range because of its wide cultivation throughout South East Asia in the past, and its subsequent naturalisation. The consensus of opinion seems to suggest that it probably originates in Northern Burma and adjacent territories, although it could equally well be native to Central and Eastern China.

Heligan boasts a considerable collection of these palms, both in the Northern Gardens and in the Jungle. Most of these would have been planted just before 1900.

The Chusan Palm was first introduced to Europe in 1830 by Philip von Siebold, who sent seeds from Japan to the Botanical Garden at Leyden. Apparently very few germinated, but of the plants produced, one was sent to Kew in 1836. It was planted in a greenhouse – being a palm, it was assumed it would not be hardy. It is reported that by 1860 it was 28ft tall, and by the end of the century it was dead! In 1843 Robert Fortune had seen this palm growing on the island of Chusan, on his way to the mouth of the Yangtze River. He gave it the vernacular name which we still use. In 1849 he dispatched a few plants to England from Chekiang, recommending that they be planted outside, as the species appeared to be hardy. One was planted at Kew, where it still survives, and another was presented to the Prince Consort. This was planted at Osborne House on the Isle of Wight, and by 1979 was 40ft tall; unfortunately it was blown down in the Spring of 2003. The earliest commercial distribution of the Chusan Palm in the British Isles was from Glendinnings Nursery when, in 1860, they auctioned plants grown from seed collected by Fortune in the Ningpo area of Chekiang. This evidence gives an age limit for the potentially oldest plants in general cultivation, but it is not known if any of them survive. It seems unlikely.

Clockwise from left: Spent leaf bases clothe the trunk of Trachycarpus fortunei*; one of our oldest specimens; the flowers*

The Chusan Palm is capable of reaching a height of 65ft+ when growing under favourable conditions, but this will take a considerable time, and it therefore needs the time, space and headroom for development. It develops a slender, erect, cylindrical trunk which is more or less 4 inches in diameter, and which does not increase in girth with age. It is remarkable that this slender trunk maintains its strength and rigidity. The trunk is characterised by the coarse, dark-coloured, horsehair-like fibres which clothe and encircle it completely, making it appear to be more substantial than it really is. These are the remains of the spent leaf bases. They persist and continue to clothe the trunk, and give it a shaggy appearance right from ground level, whatever its age. This palm has the typical, virtually circular, fan-shaped leaves on a leaf stalk about 3ft long. The leaves have a life of three to four years, and as they die off they droop and form a skirt of dead leaves below the crown.

It is virtually impossible to assess the age of a palm with any accuracy, as palms do not produce growth rings or any other similarly relevant indicators. The height is thus merely a reflection of the highs and lows of the growing conditions it has experienced. The only useful indicators are planting records or other relevant historical landmarks. At Heligan we can postulate that all our Chusan Palms, which have survived from earlier vintage, are unlikely to be more than +/-110 years old – as the Great Blizzard of April 1891 would have done for any young plants which might have existed at that time. Any remaining trees would thus have been planted out since then, and the indications are that, certainly in the Jungle, plantings would have been slightly later than this – but well before the First World War.

Chaenomeles cathayensis

The fruit (above) and flowers (right), both showing thorns, of Chaenomeles cathayensis

Chaenomeles cathayensis – a species of ornamental Quince – is a widespread native in Central China. But although it was introduced over 200 years ago (when and by whom is unknown), it is still uncommon in cultivation. Its local Asiatic cousins – collectively the Japonica – are well known, and numerous cultivars have been selected. This recognition is most likely due to their smaller size, compact habit and colourful flowers, which make them much more suitable for the average-sized, contemporary garden.

The one existing plant of this Quince at Heligan is almost certainly more than 100 years old. It stands on the corner of the bed opposite the *Rhododendron falconeri*, close to the Head Gardener's Office.

As the large and spectacular fruits ripen in the Autumn, they never fail to be noticed and draw comment. In general, flowering in the Spring and fruit production in the Autumn are both prolific. However, this productivity probably reflects the maturity of our plant, and the fact that it has not been pruned for decades – if at all.

This particular Quince is a large, fairly coarse-looking, sparsely branched, almost upright but, nowadays, scandent, deciduous shrub to about 15ft in height, but which has flopped, over the years, to cover an area of about 40 square yards. Its pattern of growth in its Heligan situation has been constrained by the competition from neighbouring shrubs and overhanging trees.

The dark, chocolate- to purple-brown-barked branches are armoured with formidable, shortly pointed, 1½-ins long thorns. The leaves are alternate, with very short leaf stalks, and are getting on for 4 inches long. They are narrow-lanceolate in shape, with finely toothed margins, and are mid-green in colour with a bronze tint when young.

The flowers are large and flattish (about 1½ins in diameter), and are produced in bunches of two or three. They are virtually stalkless and five-petalled. The petals are white – very slightly flushed salmon pink with ageing. The flowers are produced before the leaves in March, on the previous season's wood. These flowers are self-fertile – which allows this single plant to fruit so well.

The fruits are large (more or less 6ins long and half as wide) and somewhat lemon-shaped – initially they are green, but ripen to yellow by about mid-November when they become noticeably aromatic. The fruits have a very short, strong stalk and are tenacious – remaining attached on the tree and eventually falling in the New Year.

The fruits can be used in cooking – and when used sparingly will add a subtly different nuance of flavour to an apple pie. They can also be used to make jelly and 'cheese' (traditional Quince preserve), or a couple or so can be kept in a bowl to scent a room.

Ficus carica 'Brown Turkey'

The original Fig on the south-facing wall of the Flower Garden (above), and the fruit (below)

Fig cultivation in Britain reached its zenith in the late nineteenth century, when figs became a popular fruit in the walled gardens and greenhouses of the wealthy. The Fig House at Heligan first appeared on a map by Thomas Gray in 1810. Figs were generally grown in lean-to or three-quarter span houses, with one tree often filling an entire glasshouse. The main issue, however, was how to contain their enthusiastic growth without compromising fruitfulness. Roots were usually constricted in a sunken container of brick and slate, thus diverting valuable energy into fruit rather than root development.

Today the glasshouse no longer exists (and hasn't for at least 120 years), except for bits of plaster and some shelving supports on the south-facing wall of the Flower Garden. Even so, a Brown Turkey fig still persists. Now gnarled and sprawling, it would once have been impeccably fan-trained against a whitewashed wall. Figs are amazingly robust and long-lived trees and are tolerant of hard pruning. Indeed we have spent the last few years attempting to coax our specimen back into a relatively civilised space.

Fig leaves are a bright, luscious green with rough hairs on the upper surface, and are generally deeply lobed. Their sap contains milky latex that can be irritating to skin. The fruit is ribbed, violet to light brown in colour with sweet, red-pink pulp. However, as fruit is carried terminally on wood made the previous season, pruning must be judicious. Being frost hardy Brown Turkey has become one of the most common varieties of fig grown in Britain.

Interestingly, Brown Turkey is also able to fruit on new growth, so that in warmer climates or under glass a second crop is possible in the same season. In Britain one crop a year is the norm, with a later flush of immature, pea-sized fruit usually remaining into Winter. These should be removed for they will inhibit the development of next year's fruit – which for the moment exist as tiny fruitlets lying dormant in leaf axils.

Cultivated in Turkey, the ancient Smyrna fig is still the most widely grown variety for drying.

Unlike Brown Turkey, which is self fertile, the Smyrna requires caprification, a specialised form of cross-pollination, to produce fruit. All fig flowers are inverted and gathered inside a fleshy receptacle which eventually swells to become the fruit. Pollinated seeds afford the characteristic nutty taste of dried figs.

Plagianthus betulinus

Plagianthus betulinus *near the Bee Boles (above). The flowers in Summer on a younger tree (right)*

A group of three fairly small, graceful, but otherwise unremarkable, trees has survived by the path in front of the Bee Boles. During the years of neglect the trees have become shrouded in lichens, mosses and small ferns, which grow along the upper surfaces of the more horizontal branches, and in the branch angles – making them look aged and gnarled. All this reflects, in turn, the clean, unpolluted air of the area and the local, temperate-rainforest climate.

This tree is native to most of New Zealand. The genus (consisting of only two species) is closely allied to *Hoheria*. It has conventionally been known in the United Kingdom as *Plagianthus betulinus*, but modern taxonomic quirks have decided it should properly be *P. regius*. Our specimens seem to have thrived in the local climate, which is not unlike that of its native habitat. It is a Ribbonwood (cf. *Hoheria sexstylosa*), and in this case the tissues underneath the bark were used by the Maoris for ties, in a similar fashion to raffia, or for making cloth, as if it were a flax. It grows in riparian habitats – beside rivers – up to elevations of 1,500 feet. It is also distinguished as New Zealand's largest deciduous tree.

In the way that many New Zealand plants do, this Plagianthus goes through distinct growth habit phases during its lifetime, varying as it progresses through juvenility to maturity.

The juvenile phase gives no indication of the type of tree that it will eventually become. It is characterised by developing as a light, airy shrub of graceful appearance, with interlacing, fine and flexuous stems with an open, branching habit. The leaves in this phase are small, roundish and less than an inch across, and are reasonably well spaced, giving the plant a light texture.

As the tree matures, it develops an upright habit, and one single stem becomes dominant. It will reach up to 50 feet in its native stands.

The leaves in this phase become lanceolate, 2ins long and an inch wide, with a serrated edge. The flowers are produced prolifically, in dense panicles, in early Summer. Each flower is small and inconspicuous, but the billowing, cloud-like panicle of flowers becomes yellowy green. Seed production is substantial.

Its hardiness in Britain is suspect, especially when it is young; but it has survived here for over 100 years. It was introduced to cultivation in Britain in 1870, but by whom appears to be obscure.

Icons of Heligan – treasures from the past

Acknowledgements

All colour photographs in this book were taken at Heligan. We are particularly grateful to our neighbour, Charles Francis, for whom this has been a special project over the past two years.

Charles Francis, pages 11, 13, 17 (bottom), 18, 19, 20, 21, 23 (bottom), 25 (mid), 26, 27 (mid, bottom), 29 (top), 30 (mid, bottom), 31, 32, 33 (bottom), 35, 36 (bottom), 37 (bottom L), 38, 39 (bottom L), 40, 41 (mid, bottom), 43, 44 (bottom), 45, 46, 47 (top L), 48, 51 (top L), 52, 53, 54, 55, 57 (top R, bottom), 59 (top L), 61 (mid, bottom), cover

David Hastilow, pages 3, 10 (top), 14, 15, 16, 17 (top), 22, 24, 25 (top), 27 (top), 34, 47 (top R, mid L, bottom L), 49 (bottom), 50, 51 (top R), 56, 63

Trish Hogg, pages 28, 29 (bottom)

Andrea Jones, page 41 (top)

Russell May, pages 39 (top), 62 (R)

Ruth Perkins, pages 33 (top), 44 (top)

Carol Sherwood, pages 36 (top), 37 (top, bottom R)

Julian Stephens, pages 12, 23 (top), 25 (bottom), 30 (top), 39 (bottom R), 42, 49 (top), 51 (bottom), 57 (top L), 58, 59 (top R, bottom), 60 (L), 61 (top), 62 (L)

Claire Travers, page 60 (R)

Front cover photograph: Palm, Tree Fern, Ginkgo and Rhododendron © Charles Francis.
Back cover photographs: Cornus capitata – flowers, fruits and seedlings, all © Charles Francis.

Archival Images were sourced as follows:

Tab Anstice: 'Gunnera Man' inside front cover
The Rhododendrons of Sikkim-Himalaya 1849–51 (Reeve & Co., 1849–51), by J.D. Hooker: Fitch lithograph, page 3
Cornwall County Record Office: 1777 map, page 4
Hortus Veitchii: three Veitch portraits, page 7
PlantExplorers.com: E.H. Wilson and R. Fortune portraits, page 7
A Passion for Plants: The Treseders of Truro, by Suzanne Treseder (Alison Hodge, 2004): James Treseder portrait, page 7
'Journal kept by David Douglas during his Travels in North America 1823–1827': David Douglas portrait, page 7
Big Tree Country website: portrait of Archibald Menzies, page 7
Himalayan Journals, by Sir J.D. Hooker (Ward, Lock & Bowden Ltd, 1893): all images on pages 8 and 9
Heligan Gardens Limited Archive: 1844 sketch, page 4; H.H. Tremayne miniature, page 5; sepia photo of Italian Garden (from an album loaned from New Zealand), page 10
Tremayne Family: all other archival images

Our thanks go to all contributors.

We have endeavoured to establish permissions for use of all material. We apologise for possible omissions and invite corrections for future editions.

The Plant Location Map inside the back cover was created by Russell May

First published in 2007 for **Heligan Gardens Ltd**. by **Alison Hodge**, 2 Clarence Place, Penzance, Cornwall TR18 2QA.

Reprinted 2008.

ISBN 9780906720530

British Library Cataloguing-in-Publication Data
A catalogue record for this book is available from the British Library.

Designed and originated by
BDP – Book Development and Production, Penzance, Cornwall

Printed and bound in China on paper produced with elemental chlorine-free pulp, harvested from managed sustainable forests.

The Lost Gardens of Heligan
are open daily all year round from 10am (closed Christmas Eve and Christmas Day).

For further information please contact:
The Lost Gardens of Heligan, Pentewan, St Austell, Cornwall PL26 6EN, England
Tel: 01726 845100; email: info@heligan.com, or visit www.heligan.com